A Pre-Reader
for the
Foundation Degree
in
Health and Social Care Practice

•

Margaret Ann Bannister

Illustrated by Pam Grant

A Pre-Reader for the Foundation Degree in Health and Social Care Practice
Margaret Ann Bannister

ISBN: 978-1-905539-68-0

First published 2011

Illustrations © Pam Grant 2011

British Library Cataloguing in Publication Data
A catalogue record for this book is available from the British Library

Notice

Clinical practice and medical knowledge constantly evolve. Standard safety precautions must be followed, but, as knowledge is broadened by research, changes in practice, treatment and drug therapy may become necessary or appropriate. Readers must check the most current product information provided by the manufacturer of each drug to be administered and verify the dosages and correct administration, as well as contraindications. It is the responsibility of the practitioner, utilising the experience and knowledge of the patient, to determine dosages and the best treatment for each individual patient. Any brands mentioned in this book are as examples only and are not endorsed by the publisher. Neither the publisher nor the authors assume any liability for any injury and/or damage to persons or property arising from this publication.

To contact M&K Publishing write to:
M&K Update Ltd · The Old Bakery · St. John's Street
Keswick · Cumbria CA12 5AS
Tel: 01768 773030 · Fax: 01768 781099
publishing@mkupdate.co.uk
www.mkupdate.co.uk

1006577074

Designed by Mary Blood
Typeset in 9pt Helvetica Neue Light
Printed in England by Ferguson Print, Keswick.

A Pre-Reader for the Foundation Degree
in Health and Social Care Practice

Other Health & Social Care books from M&K include:

Nurses and Their Patients: Informing practice through psychodynamic insights
ISBN: 978-1-905539-31-4

Spiritual Assessment in Healthcare Practice
ISBN: 978-1-905539-27-7

Perspectives on Death and Dying
ISBN: 978-1-905539-21-5

The Clinician's Guide to Chronic Disease Management
for Long-Term Conditions: A cognitive-behavioural approach
ISBN: 978-1-905539-15-4

Research Issues in Health and Social Care
ISBN: 978-1-905539-20-8

Identification and Treatment of Alcohol Dependency
ISBN: 978-1-905539-16-1

Preventing and Reducing Aggression & Violence in Health and Social Care:
A holistic approach
ISBN: 978-1-905539-57-4

Improving Patient Outcomes
ISBN: 978-1-905539-06-2

Ward-Based Critical Care
ISBN: 978-1-905539-03-1

The ECG Workbook 2/e
ISBN: 978-1-905539-77-2

Contents

Acknowledgements

Many people have contributed to the writing of this book. Without doubt my work with Boston College has enabled me to develop my own knowledge and opened up the possibility of offering support to students embarking on a programme in higher education. A few of the activities used in this book were developed for my teaching with the college and as such are accredited to the college.

Books do not get written without the support of many people. Family, friends, colleagues and other authors all impact on the writing process. I am indebted to my family and friends, Ken Bannister, William and Angela Rimmer, Peter Rimmer for his illustration briefs, and James Rimmer, Susan Gregory, Hannah Gregory, Rosanna Smith and Marion Holland. I also want to personally thank Mike Roberts and his team, Sue Brackenbury, Jenny Smith and her team at Boston College, and Ken Ripley, the Practice Educator for Assistant Practitioners at United Lincoln Hospital Trust. This book would never have been conceived of if it hadn't been for all my students, and in particular Susan Allen, Jacqueline Auckland, Barbara Charlton, Joanne Gosling, Collette Hammond and Sharon Miller. I am honoured to have had contact with David Seedhouse and Susan Jeffers, and thank them both for their support. Thanks too, to the publishers Wiley-Blackwell for their permission to reproduce David Seedhouse's case history from Seedhouse, D. (2009) *Ethics: The Heart of Health Care*.

Introduction

The purpose of this pre-reader is just that – a book that aims to provide the necessary knowledge and tools to enable healthcare workers to study at foundation degree level. It needs to be acknowledged here that different National Health Service (NHS) Trusts use different titles for non-qualified care staff. Different pay bands also determine different titles. For instance, in Lincolnshire, where I now lecture, there are healthcare assistants at band 2 and healthcare support workers at band 3, while some areas use the titles nursing assistants, nursing auxiliaries or care workers. Therefore, for the purposes of this book, I will use the generic term 'healthcare worker' to encompass them all. It should also be noted that different specialities uses different terms for the person receiving care, and to avoid confusion I will call all receivers of care 'clients'. Different universities also use different titles for the programmes that enable healthcare workers to gain the foundation degree in order to become assistant practitioners in the workplace. Therefore I will refer to the programme as 'foundation degree' only.

Throughout my teaching on the degree programme with Boston College, it has become apparent that students are recruited from the workplace (mainly the NHS) with little prior experience of higher education. A minority of students have gained some qualifications since their compulsory education; however, these tend to be national vocational qualifications (NVQs). NVQs involve totally different skills from those required to complete a foundation degree at a university. To this end, this book will not teach theory because that is the purpose of the foundation degree programme; instead it aims to teach skills, attitudes and behaviours that are conducive to study, and enable students to make the transition from healthcare worker to trainee assistant practitioner (TAP), and ultimately it is hoped that these skills will be transferable and serve them throughout their careers as assistant practitioners.

The NHS has spent the last few decades in an almost constant state of change, from the emergence of quality assurance in the 1980s to the fairly recent decision to make nursing an entirely graduate profession. It has to be acknowledged that highly qualified nurses are a necessary component of healthcare in the twenty-first century; however, it also needs to be acknowledged that employing all graduate nursing staff will leave a gap in the workforce that will need to be appropriately filled by the role of the assistant practitioner (AP).

The assistant practitioner role came into being approximately nine years ago and yet, within many workplace settings, the role remains shrouded in mystery. In Lincolnshire, training of assistant practitioners began in 2007. Since then, 54 students have graduated and a further 51 have started training. This is an exciting time for healthcare workers in this area, as they have a unique opportunity to be at the forefront of healthcare, supported by a foundation degree. It is also an exciting time for healthcare workers nationwide, with the assistant practitioner role developing, providing an appropriate and much-needed level of care throughout the NHS. As lifelong learners, these assistant practitioners will be able to progress further in education, bringing a valuable skill mix to the workplace.

Across the full range of health and social care settings, each student group is diverse and has many different abilities. Students need to be able to recognise these skills in themselves and within the group to make the most of their natural resources. Studying health and social care requires the student to have an awareness of values and beliefs, to think laterally and critically, and to be reflective, and responsive to the needs not only of the client but also of other team members across the whole field. The foundation degree programme will encourage the development of knowledge and skills that enable each individual to become a valuable member of the multidisciplinary team. This process changes the individual in several ways. Some people refer to education as a journey, with the programme taking us on a journey of discovery not only of the taught elements but also of ourselves and our developing confidence. We change as we learn, further developing our skills, knowledge and confidence. This change is a gradual process that we may not easily recognise in ourselves. By developing self-awareness and fully understanding our own way of being, we can embrace the change, move forward in our careers and enjoy the benefits of our progression. Those around us, including our family and friends, will recognise this change more easily and therefore it is imperative to keep them involved in the process from the start, enabling the development of both personal and professional relationships. When you enter higher education as a mature student, you need to be prepared for study and be prepared to change, and you need to encourage those around you to travel with you and enjoy the process.

This book includes many activities to help you develop the skills you need for study and self-development. Use them fully, write out your answers, think deeply about the suggestions, and record your responses. If you re-visit the activities throughout your programme of study, the changes will be noticeable; you will have a record of your skills at the onset of the programme and those you are developing. It may be useful to produce a portfolio of the activities as you work through this book. This would be good practice for developing portfolios, which is a necessary part of your new life as a student, and it would be useful for collecting evidence for your workplace competencies and continuous professional development. As lifelong learners, we can easily fall into the trap of assuming that we will learn by reading through an exercise, and not actively participating. However, that is rarely the case. Only by participating fully can we generate our own ideas and reinforce our learning in a concrete way. Very few of us learn by reading alone; therefore I would actively encourage you to work through the activities as you read through this book.

For my sisters, Susan Gregory and Gillian Broadwith

Chapter one
Preparation for Study

Undertaking a programme of study as an adult involves becoming an active participant in the learning process. It cannot be assumed that everything required will be taught. Learning does not occur by osmosis but by the involved commitment of all concerned. Fortunately for students in the twenty-first century, educators recognise the need to involve students, and many professionals have developed tried and tested methods to be used as tools for learning. As with everything, it would be churlish not to use these methods, particularly if there is one method that suits your particular learning style. Also, as with any learning, it is never enough merely to read about the topic. In order to ensure learning takes place, the student has to engage with the material or learning tool, practise using it and become comfortable with it. An example here that is unrelated to study in a formal way is my husband's attempts to complete Sudoku puzzles. An avid Sudoku puzzler myself, it takes me a matter of minutes to complete a moderately hard puzzle. My husband, after noting my enjoyment, decided he wanted some of that pleasure and attempted his first puzzle. After several hours on an easy puzzle he gave up in frustration, unable to complete it, even with tips from me. Some time later, trying again, he was dismayed to find he still could not do these puzzles, and was not impressed when I informed him that his inability to complete them came down to his lack of practice at actually doing them. He needs to practise them regularly in order to learn the process. Practice does make perfect. My husband still only attempts them once in a while and still suffers the frustration of non-achievement.

Spend some time looking into techniques that make your own life easier. Practise using different methods, such as lists, a notice board, mind mapping or timetables (see Chapter 1 and Chapter 3). Practise reading, note-taking, storing and retrieving material. Practise writing, paraphrasing and referencing. They are all skills to develop through your periods of study and all require practice. Try not to fall into the trap of photocopying tools, articles and materials that may prove to be useful – and then never get round to actually using them.

Naturally, there are many other practical tools you can use to prepare yourself for study. Organisation and planning will become prime aspects of your life from now on. The sooner you develop these skills, the sooner you will become comfortable with your learning schedules. It sounds a simple idea to get yourself organised, but again actually 'doing it' takes time. It needs thinking through and explaining to all the people who share your life.

Learning styles

A good starting place is to explore your individual learning style. A search on the internet will reveal many questionnaire tests with printable advice to facilitate your learning. It would be advisable to revisit and review these as you progress through your course. Discovering your own learning style will enable you to select methods and tools that suit you. They will make life easier, but again you will need to explore them fully and practise your preferred methods in order to make them work for you. Learning is like riding a bike – very difficult initially, but improvements can be seen with practice; and even if we do not continue the activity, once learnt, the skills can be revised and used forever. Now try the exercise in Activity 1.1.

Activity 1.1

Search for a learning styles tool on the internet. Complete the questionnaire and print out the result. Consider for a while what the result says about your own individual style. Do the suggested methods for learning suit you? Do you recognise them? Can you use them to aid your learning?

Activity A

Select one of the learning methods you are familiar with and use it to plan an essay about your work role. The essay should be a descriptive overview of what your role encompasses, the tasks undertaken, who you report to, and so on.

Plan what you would need to include.

For instance, if using a list it may include:

- The title of your role.
- Who you report to.
- Who you are responsible for.

- Tasks undertaken (this could be quite extensive).
- Your extended role.
- Your opportunities within the role.

Activity B

Now select a tool that you are not as familiar with and plan your essay using that tool.
Which one was easier to use?
Which one do you think will encourage you to research material further?
Which one makes you want to actually write the piece?

Explore the methods suggested throughout this chapter and experiment with them to develop and utilise your individual learning style.

Activity 1.1

Remember...

just reading about learning styles will not make life easier for you – only putting the associated tools to use will.

Organising your work

Space

Having a place to keep study materials enables students to be organised and be prepared for taught sessions. If you do not have a specific room to use as a study then you need somewhere in your home that you will be able to make into your own space: the dining room table, a spare bedroom or a kitchen table – whatever suits you best. If it is an area that has to be used by other people then you will need a large box in order to pack things away. As most of us need to use space occupied by others, a system for setting things out and packing them away will save time and reduce stress when searching for things. If you are lucky enough to have a study then you will only need to organise the space into a good working environment. Remember to discuss this with other members of your family in order to gain their understanding of your need for organisation. It will also make them more supportive of you if you involve them in these types of decisions. A time may come when you need to delegate tasks, and this will encourage them to support your learning (see *Time management* below).

As healthcare professionals you should also be aware of all health and safety aspects, such as moving and handling, and you may need to revise safety issues regarding computers. A search on the internet will provide useful information regarding the health aspects of sitting at a computer, or you can contact the IT specialist at your place of work or college for advice.

The space you choose for study will need good lighting and comfortable seating and there should be minimal interruptions. You will need access to writing equipment, books and journals, and a computer for word-processing and internet access. A good tip is not to allow telephones in your study space, as the temptation to answer a call from a friend who is bound to have something important to discuss can be overwhelming. Missed calls can always be caught up on later, when you are ready for some distraction.

Storage

You can use folders, box files, index cards or just a large cardboard box to store things in. As long as you list the items in some ordered way (such as alphabetically or in date order), you will be able to find anything you need at any time. You will need to carefully store all your returned assignments as evidence of completion, and some may be useful for your competency work. The modules on the foundation degree programme often overlap, so completed assignments may be useful for refreshing your memory of theoretical concepts. Feedback on your assignments will also become a useful tool for planning future assignments, so you will need access to returned work whenever you are planning for the next round of assignments (see Chapter 3). Books borrowed from libraries will need to be returned by a set date and I always find it useful to enter the return date in my diary to avoid overdue fines. I have heard of overdue fees amounting to over £30 so being organised here will save you money!

Time management

We all need time to study, but people often underestimate the amount of time required for research and assignment writing. As a student it will be advantageous to make sure that the people you live with are aware of what study time means to you. Partners or children will interrupt with questions, and the phone will need answering, as will the door. All these create distractions and disturb your study time, and it can be very difficult to return to your books following a distraction. As a student, there is nothing worse than being deeply involved in a piece of writing and being disrupted by a minor distraction, when all that was needed was a little cooperation. The foundation degree programme is very time-consuming so involve close family members from the start, explaining that it is for two years. Planning a family treat at the end will encourage them to support you.

The easy way to deal with time issues is to:

- Talk to family and friends. Explain how important your study time is, bargain for babysitting or cooking, and ensure you get people on your side to support you.
- Delegate household tasks wherever possible. You may need to negotiate, depending on your arrangements, but a previously planned reward at the end of the programme may help.
- Be specific about the times you will study. Make sure everyone knows when you would prefer not to be interrupted, and use that time wisely.
- Always have an end time for your study periods so that others know when you will be free again.
- Ignore the telephone or doorbell – you can always call people back later. They will understand and will want to support you.
- Time your study sessions and plan your work to fit the time available. You will need to build in breaks to relieve the pressure, but these also should be timed to avoid time wasting. Procrastination leads to panic!
- Keep your timetable in a prominent place so that others can see what you are doing rather than interrupting you to ask if you are busy.

Try creating a timetable of a typical week to see where you can plan to study. The chart in Fig. 1.1 (see p. 6) looks impressive, showing a time and place for every function. However, this student has built in no time for rest and relaxation, and these are very important while studying. You will need plenty of 'me time' in order to recharge your batteries and keep working productively. A good exercise would be to create several timetables to cover the varied shift patterns that you may encounter as a healthcare worker. Include college days and time with your family, as well as study time, reading time, and the all-important relaxation time. Make sure that you reward yourself regularly, to recharge your batteries and provide motivation when the going gets tough.

	Monday	Tuesday	Wednesday	Thursday	Friday	Saturday	Sunday
6–8	Work	Home	Work	Home	Home	Home	Study
8–10		College					
10–12				Study	Study		Home
12–2						Study	
2–4						Children	Children
4–6	Children	Children	Children	Children	Children		
6–8						Study	Study
8–10	Study	Study	Study	Study	Study		

Fig. 1.1: *A sample student's weekly timetable, including 'home' time (for cooking, cleaning, shopping, DIY, gardening), 'children' time, and 'study' time (time that is available for study).*

Equipment and resources

All the usual office-type materials will be useful when studying – folders, lined paper, pens, pencils, paperclips, a stapler, hole punch, and paper and ink for your printer, to name a few. You will not need all of these at the outset of the programme so spread the cost over time, buying supplies as and when you need them. A good notebook will definitely be required straight away, as the teaching will commence on day one and note-taking will be an important skill to develop from the outset (see Chapter 3). All assignments for universities have to be word-processed. Computer skills, although perhaps a little daunting at first, can soon be acquired through practice. This type of activity requires you to have a go, playing with all the options in order to familiarise yourself with them well enough to use them effectively. You could get a lesson or two, to learn about setting up a page, font types and sizes, word counts, justification, line spacing and page breaks. You will also need to be able to send and receive emails with attachments and, of course, to save them to a folder.

Working on a computer can be time-consuming initially but you will be surprised how quickly your skills will develop. The health and safety aspects need to be observed and there are many guides on the market to help you develop these much-needed skills. Some people prefer to proofread their work from hard (paper) copy, so try to save paper by re-using your print sheets (but be careful that you do not get confused about which piece you are reading!). One top tip is to make sure you always have a spare printer cartridge to hand. Running out of printer ink is a poor excuse for non-submission of work and many institutions will not accept it. Another good tip is to keep a notebook and pen with you at all times. As a student, I often struggled to find the words to describe a concept and then, when I least expected it, the words came to mind – usually in a totally unsuitable place, like a supermarket, the dentist's waiting room or on the bus travelling home from work. A small notebook and pen, which can be easily stored in a pocket or bag, will prevent that awful feeling when you return from the supermarket and cannot recall those much-needed and obviously exceptional words.

Chapter two
Preparation for Change

As a healthcare worker about to commence the trainee assistant practitioner (TAP) programme, you need to be prepared to be changed. There is no way to measure the changes that will take place, but you will find out that life will never be the same again. Having spoken to students throughout their training and on completion, I have been privileged to share in the acknowledgement of change. It is very difficult to quantify, however. It most definitely does occur and I genuinely believe it is for the better. One student, mid-way through her second year of the programme, stated: 'I did things – even if I was unsure – because I was told to. Now I don't. I do things I know I am capable of doing and refuse when asked to do things I do not understand.'

Where once, as a healthcare worker, you functioned in the workplace because 'that was how it was done', you will begin to question what you do on a daily basis. You will search for the reasoning and evidence behind your actions and ensure that your practice is grounded in theory for the good of the client. As a trainee assistant practitioner, you will become a reflective practitioner, with the knowledge and skills to practise as a professional. You will have the wherewithal to challenge poor practice, and the resources to improve practice in an evidence-based professional manner.

Undertaking a programme of study such as the foundation degree changes you as a whole person. It broadens your outlook, widens your knowledge and encourages you to look at things in a totally different way. Study not only changes you professionally, into a reflective evidence-based practitioner, but it also brings about changes in your personal life. Many students have mentioned this, stating that their partners or family or friends do not understand them any more. They have all 'stood still', while the student has undergone a massive developmental process. Unfortunately for some, this can have detrimental consequences, such as the breakdown of a marriage, which can impact on the student's ability to study. Being aware of this process and the possible consequences means you can embrace the changes fully and make them a shared experience for you, your colleagues, your family and your friends, thus making your graduation day a celebration for all concerned. Involving everyone around you in the process will enable them to understand and embrace the changes that take place.

To make the process easier, students need to open up their own communication channels, keeping everyone involved and informed and enabling everyone to be open to the changes that may occur. Becoming an assistant practitioner within the NHS today is an exciting prospect for those undertaking training and also for the family and friends supporting them. It will open doors to further education, develop confidence, and increase self-esteem. By involving everyone, all your relationships will develop throughout the process.

The more we learn, the more we change. Learning broadens our outlook, gives us confidence, encourages inquisitiveness, and extends our knowledge. Students who complete the foundation degree programme commonly state how different they are at the end of the two years. Not only have they become questioning, reflective and professional practitioners in their workplace, but they also report big changes in their private lives. This is quite noticeable in students on this programme as they move from working almost by rote, to being active professionals who question the way they function and the logic behind their actions. They even take the theory, values and attitudes of care work into their private lives. Once they do this, they understand people far better, appreciate the diversity of people far more, and can be very different from the person who enrolled on the programme. Each of these students develops confidence and self-esteem, which has a positive effect on their relationships throughout their whole lives. By involving everyone, and sharing the experience, the end result can be that their study has far-reaching, positive consequences for all.

Reflective practice

Reflective practice is one of the most valuable tools that you will gain on your journey to becoming a lifelong learner. Many people are somewhat derogatory about reflective practice, while others appreciate it for the useful tool that it is. I genuinely believe that those who scorn it have not practised it sufficiently to develop their own style and make it a natural part of themselves. Having taught reflective practice to the majority of our foundation degree students at Boston College, it has become very apparent that the students who embrace reflective practice are those who really benefit from it.

Reflective practice needs to be used on a regular basis to enable you to gain the most from it. This is particularly so when you begin to learn about the various models or cycles of reflective practice within your programme of study. Some models can be quite complex, with seven or eight stages, and as such they need a determined effort in order to appreciate their value. Without frequent use, reflective practice becomes a chore, when in reality it is a valuable tool for learning and self-development.

There are many forms of reflection, and using theoretical frameworks will achieve the desired result. Some models will suit different situations, so it will be necessary for you to explore several of the theoretical models during your study to ascertain which one works best for you. As a student, you need to use these freely and often. Eventually you will settle on one or two that best suit your own needs.

I appreciate that at this point I am being very repetitive, yet this message needs to be repeated for most of the tools in this book – reflective practice needs *practice*. It is no use reading about it once, using a textbook to complete a cycle, and then deciding reflective practice is not for you. You need to try out different methods. Spend time applying different methods to the same experience. It takes time and practice to find a method that works best for you. I also appreciate that, as a trainee assistant practitioner, time is of the essence. You will have one study day per week, your usual shifts in the workplace, and your personal lives to manage. To this end, it would be a good idea to start developing these skills now, before you start your programme. If for no other reason, it will get you used to allocating time several times a week in order to reflect and/ or study (see Chapter 1).

Free-writing

Reflection does not have to follow a theoretical framework to be effective. It can involve 'free-writing' about a particular event. By free-writing about an event or experience, you will be looking at it closely, exploring how it happened, why it happened, what the outcome was, and – most importantly – whether the outcome could have been different. By using reflection, you are examining how you behaved in a given situation and also how others have behaved; you are looking to see if the situation could have been changed to lead to a better outcome for one or all of the people involved. It will give an insight into how you behave and react and also how others behave and react, creating a deeper understanding of why we all behave as we do. In this way, reflective practice creates a better understanding of yourself and how you react in different situations. Activity 2.1 gives you an opportunity to try out free-writing.

Activity 2.1

Think of something that has happened recently in your workplace.

Take a pen and paper and free-write about it.

You may want to follow some guided questions to start with, such as:

What actually happened?
When did the event take place?
Where did the event take place?
Who else was involved?
What was the outcome of the event?

Now think about something that has happened in your private life and repeat the exercise.

Keeping a journal

By entering all your reflective pieces into one notebook (or journal), you will produce a vast array of material that will be invaluable for your self-development. Once you have collected a dozen entries or so, try to take time to read through them all. It is very likely that you will be able to pick out patterns that will highlight a particular skill or trait that you possess. If you feel it is a useful skill, you will then be able to recognise it and develop it further. Or you may recognise a trait that is not particularly desirable, in which case you can plan how to overcome it and change it.

Whether you are writing about your private or working life, make entries in your journal consecutively, dating each one for easy reference, and keep them all in a safe place. Writing in a journal like this will promote your individual self-development and may provide useful evidence for future work or study. You do not need to consider confidentiality issues with a private journal because it is for your eyes only. But if parts are to be used for assignment work, appraisals or competency work then you will need to ensure that you are respecting the confidentiality of all involved.

Chapter three
Basic Study Skills

There are myriad books on the market to provide you with study skills. The intention of this chapter is to open your mind to the possibility of developing a few of the most basic skills in order to make study as straightforward as possible. Studying on the foundation degree programme is made more difficult by the demands of shift working and very busy personal lives. Students should develop their skills to make the most of all their learning opportunities, in order to make life easier at work, at college and at home. With the best will in the world, we are all tested regularly by the challenges that life throws at us. To be a student, to manage work pressures and to maintain a 'normal' lifestyle requires students to be flexible, to be prepared to rearrange things at a moment's notice, and to know how to use appropriate stress management techniques.

Before researching study skills further, take some time to consider what works for you in your everyday life. Are you the kind of person who writes a shopping list and then forgets to take it to the supermarket? Does this mean that list-making is not for you? Think about what happens. Do you manage to buy everything on your list without referring to it, or do you miss items that you really needed? If the former is true for you, it may mean that the process of making a list sets the information firmly in your mind, so list-making could be a useful aid to study for you. When creating such a list do you use words alone, or do you draw pictures or doodles alongside the items? If so, which works best for recalling the items – the words or the pictures? What was it that prompted you to remember? You will be able to relate this to your personal learning style, mentioned in Chapter 1.

Time management

Time management is covered in more detail in Chapter 1. However, as mentioned above, experiences from your everyday life can be used to develop this skill further.

Finding a method that suits you is necessary to success here. If a timetable works well for you, then a small folder that is easily transportable should do the trick. I personally manage my time using my diary and small sticky notes. It is certainly not a neat and tidy method but it works for me so I am loathe to change it (even though it drives others mad – especially my husband!). Organisational skills, specific study skills, flexibility in your personal life and establishing sources of help will all contribute towards the basic study skills you will employ over the programme of study. When you are organising your time, do not forget that you need to include rest and relaxation time. An exhausted student will struggle to achieve.

Organisational skills

Consider how organised you are in your home life. If you needed to prove you had paid a six-month-old household bill, how long would it take you to find it? If you could retrieve it immediately, then you are clearly very organised and will find storing material, cataloguing and retrieving evidence a straightforward task.

If you couldn't find it immediately, you will need to develop systems to make things easier for you, and to keep your stress levels at a minimum. This will come down to trial and error. You will need to spend time working on systems to find the one that will work best for you. Try using index cards for cataloguing references, books and articles, for example. Make lists of the books you use for note-taking, ensuring that all the appropriate details are recorded for referencing purposes. Use files or folders for class notes and keep a folder for completed assignments, as some may be useful for cross-referencing purposes in later assignments.

The same points can apply to travelling to new locations. You may be one of those people who can drive to a new location and arrive punctually, with minimal stress. However, some people need more time and help finding new places to prevent them arriving very stressed and flustered. If you turn me around three times in my own home I lose my bearings and need time to reorient myself. I know that I need to plan journeys carefully, even those I have done before, in fine detail, in order to arrive in a calm state and be able to function well on arrival.

Reading skills

Reading takes time and you need to take time to read. In your lectures, let's imagine you are given the equivalent of a tennis-ball-sized amount of information. Further reading, discussion and research will make that tennis ball into a hot air balloon! For more on this, see *Assignment writing* below.

The skill of reading also needs practice. Start with small sections, read them through, make notes and paraphrase the information, ensuring you have understood what you have read. Gradually increase the amount you read. One tip that I have always found a little odd is that you should be interested in what you are reading. Obviously, interest will fuel your motivation to read the material. However, I would be surprised if you were truly interested in all the material you need to read in order to complete assignments. As some information may involve a more dedicated effort, you need to build your ability to concentrate so that you fully understand what you are reading.

Reading in order to write an assignment also needs practice. It is very easy to become distracted whilst reading by something not totally relevant, so you need to be disciplined whilst reading for assignment work. Initially you should determine what information is relevant to that particular assignment. Start with your assignment brief and look for other clues. The syllabus of the module may be helpful, as may the related learning outcomes. Make sure you understand what it is you need to write about and then break it down into smaller pieces. This should give you distinct areas to start reading around.

Reading for an assignment

For this section I will use an entirely fictitious brief for an assignment. Consider the following essay brief:

'Discuss how communication skills can enhance the experience of a client within your care setting.'

This is how you should approach such a brief:

- First, check the syllabus to link listed topics to the brief.
- Second, check which learning outcomes are relevant. It may be useful to print these out and pin them up in your study area to constantly remind you of the details.
- Third, brainstorm the topic or mind map the areas you need to research (Buzan and Buzan, 2003). For more on mind mapping, see *Assignment writing* below.

The most obvious topic in this brief is *communication skills*. It may be that you work in a specialist area in which all the clients have special needs; therefore an understanding of these would be beneficial. Within any communication interaction there will be barriers (things that prevent effective communication). The practitioner needs to be aware of these barriers in order to reduce them as much as possible. The brief also mentions the *experience* of the client. As will be discussed in Chapter 5, everyone is an individual and has different values, perceptions and experiences. This means the assignment will also draw on values, beliefs and perceptions, with the individuality and diversity of people being important aspects of the work. Therefore the concepts that may need to be researched for this written piece might be:

- communication skills (list specific skills)
- client needs
- barriers to communication
- beliefs, values and perceptions
- equality and diversity.

From an assignment brief consisting of a single sentence, we have already developed quite a wide area for research. This demonstrates that the reading needs to be very selective – relating to the communication skills needed with one particular client in one specific care setting. It would be impossible to read all the published material on each of the listed areas, and the resulting assignment would have a word count that would terrify the most hardened tutor. Therefore, restricting your reading to specific areas will save you time and keep you focused on what is needed for the assignment.

A simple way to organise the development of your reading skill is to follow these basic steps:

1. Read the piece through at least once without making notes or questioning it.
2. Read it again while thinking about the main points. What is it telling you? Does it point you towards different areas that may need further exploration?
3. Read it again, making notes as you go.

This should provide a basic overview of the piece and you can decide if the material is suitable for your assignment work. You could add a fourth step: to write about the material in your own words to show your understanding. When reading in this way, it is most important to write down the details needed for referencing and the bibliography (in fact it would be wise to do this at step 1).

Assessing the brief

The precise words used in the assignment brief also indicate the direction that the work should take. During the planning stage of your assignment it may be useful to underline the words that dictate the way the work should be written.

Here are some commonly used terms:

- **Describe**: This means explaining what it is. For example, describing a model of health involves writing about all the components of the model.
- **Compare**: This involves looking at the topics and how they work with or against each other. In a comparison of models of health, for example, you might explore the similarities or differences between two or more models.
- **Discuss**: This indicates that you should explore by creating an argument around the component parts of the brief.
- **Analyse**: More depth is required to explore the component parts of the whole. You should develop an argument as to how the component parts work together (or not) and offer your own views, if required. Using the opinions of theorists to support the argument gives more credibility to the work at this stage.
- **Evaluate**: Evaluating means making judgements, and deciding whether or not something is effective. Again, theoretical support is needed.

Keeping track of references

I once had a lecturer who suggested heading the pages of my notebook with the book's title, so that notes were kept together, with the reference details at the top. In practice, I often found that one page was never enough for the notes from one book, so I would use the first few pages of the notebook to record details of all the books (names of the author or authors, the date of publication, the title, the place it was published and the name of the publisher), labelling each book A, B, C, and so on. Thereafter any notes I made or direct quotes would be numbered through my notebook with codes like B97 or D126. Box 3.1 shows the kind of content found in the first few pages of my notebook.

Box 3.1 Noting down reference sources

The first pages will contain details of the information source, such as:

Page 1
A   Woods, B. (2000). *Basics in Psychology,* 2nd edn. Oxon, Hodder and Stoughton.

Page 2
B Frankland, A. and Saunders, P. (1995). *Next Steps in Counselling.* Herefordshire, PCCS Books.

Page 3
C   Jasper, M. (2003). *Beginning Reflective Practice. Foundations in Nursing and Health Care.* Cheltenham, Nelson Thornes.

Subsequent pages will contain the information or quotes from those sources, numbered in sequence:

Page 4
C 37 SWOB analysis enables us to draw attention to how we cope with challenges in life. We often focus on the negatives and we should look at them in a different way.

Page 5
A 32 "our self-concept may affect the way we see ourselves" *(a direct quote).*

In this way I collect research for my assignment and can easily see where I have found the information and have all the referencing details to hand. The majority of universities follow the Harvard system of referencing but you should be aware that there are several versions of this system so make sure you follow the appropriate guidelines.

As a student, you will need to devise a system for recording information sources that will work for you. The main points to remember are:

- Ensure you note the reference details of whatever you read.
- Read selectively, keeping focused on the topic at hand.
- Allow yourself plenty of time.

Discussing the assignment

While you are reading and collecting the relevant information, it will aid your understanding if you can discuss the material you are assembling. Mentors, colleagues, peers and family members can all be helpful in this process. Explain what it is you are researching and try to give them an overview. The swapping of experiences will aid your understanding and help you get the information into written form. Discussion can be particularly useful if there is a concept that you are struggling to understand.

Remember...

if it is a sensitive topic then you should respect the thoughts of others and not be overly critical.

You can take away others' experiences and think about how they may differ from your own, then draw your own conclusions as to how the information may work for you. You do not have to use materials or ideas generated by others in these discussions. They will simply broaden your own thinking to help you understand difficult concepts and to enable you to develop critical thought processes around the topic you are exploring.

Unfortunately we are not always able to arrange the time or have the people available to discuss everything we would like to cover. If you are struggling to understand a concept, and cannot discuss it with colleagues, then try writing it out as if you were explaining the idea to an imaginary person. Once written, leave it for a day or so, then read through it again to see if this helps clarify things in your mind. Your lecturer will always be willing to discuss things with you and may even arrange workshop sessions where you can discuss particular issues with your peers.

Mind mapping for the assignment

Mind mapping is the brain-child of Tony and Barry Buzan, who wrote *The Mind Map Book* (BBC Worldwide, 2003), in which the brain's ability to develop learning was explored. Years of work produced the concept of mind mapping, putting the topic being studied in the centre of a web of related key words (Buzan and Buzan, 2003). Radiating arms link the key words to create an overall view that can easily be recalled as required. I personally used it with great success during examinations and would recommend that students try mind mapping for themselves because it concentrates the mind on the topic in question. In the sample assignment above (see p. 18), the mind map would show communication skills in the centre, with the following arms radiating outwards:

- Service users
- Barriers
- Beliefs
- Equality and diversity.

From each of these key concepts, further links would be added to explore each of them more widely still. The completed mind map would have four areas of concentrated points, each concentrating on the specific areas that need researching. Depending on your particular learning style, the mind map could also be embellished with pictures or symbols that would prompt recall if used for revision purposes.

Writing the assignment

An activity I developed while working with the foundation degree students at Boston College involved viewing the assignment writing process as a jigsaw. The students were initially encouraged to complete a child's jigsaw (of cartoon princess characters) using the picture clues alone. Once completed, they had to break the jigsaw up and turn all the pieces face down on the table. They then had to complete the jigsaw 'upside down' without the picture clues. This was then related to the assignment writing process, whereby each piece of the jigsaw was one necessary component of the complete assignment. The component parts of an assignment are summarised in Box 3.2.

Box 3.2 Component parts of an assignment

- **Lectures**
- **Assignment brief**
- **Learning outcomes**
- **Reading (books, journals, articles, papers, internet)**
- **Discussion**
- **Tutor**
- **Mentor**
- **Peers**
- **Colleagues**

Assignment writing is a game that you need to learn to play in order to meet the requirements of the programme. It involves collecting, sorting, thinking and arranging the available material in a certain way. The way it is organised is defined by the assessment brief, which may ask you to describe, compare, analyse and evaluate the given material.

The learning outcomes need to be met within the piece and word counts need to be adhered to, with most universities allowing 10% leeway either side.

Finally, writing the assignment can be likened to putting icing on a cake. You have worked hard researching the material, and with a little planning the actual writing can be an enjoyable experience. Writing simply involves bringing together all the preparatory work into a coherent whole. Having an overall plan, such as a mind map or list, will aid the process, but each student will develop their own way of bringing the assignment together to create the required whole.

Structuring the essay

Many printed texts describe writing skills. It is beyond the scope of this book to cover all of them, but essentially an assignment is made up of the introduction, the main body, and the conclusion.

The introduction

This speaks for itself – it introduces the reader (that is, the assessor!) to the subject being discussed. It offers the student an opportunity to grab the attention of the reader and encourages him or her to read on. A few sentences describing what will be covered may not inspire someone to read on – try to be inventive in the way you introduce topics.

The main body

This will contain paragraphs covering the main points for the assignment. One point may need several paragraphs, but each one should be linked to the next, to ensure flow through the work, using a linking sentence either at the start or end of a paragraph (Northedge, 1990). Linking your themes and indicating whether the next paragraph is supporting or opposing the last will enhance your writing and motivate the reader to continue. Key words in the original brief will indicate the content of the paragraphs (such as *describing, analysing, comparing*) and the student will need to ensure that they structure their writing accordingly.

The conclusion

This should bring together everything you have written throughout the piece and again – according to the wording of the brief – make judgements about the material discussed.

Being a confident writer

Check out books on study skills (see the *Further reading* section, pp. 75–6) and explore which methods suit you best. Again it is a case of practice making perfect. We often read about a skill and think it sounds like a good way of working but in practice it may not suit us. Exploring different techniques will help you develop their own writing skills and style and your own way of compiling an assignment.

A difficult part of the assignment-writing process is to develop confidence in your writing. Many students say, when they submit their final pieces of work in the last semester, that they enjoyed their last assignment and were confident when writing it. There may well be a psychological factor here, in that it is the final piece to be submitted, but it always seems a shame that they do not enjoy completing and submitting their earlier assignments.

Having studied in various situations myself, I discovered enjoyment in assignment writing and even sitting examinations in my penultimate year of study with the Open University. I can confirm, it can be an enjoyable experience! Somehow, the penny finally dropped and I realised I was only being assessed on 'taught' material and that I would not have to produce evidence that I did not know about. This sounds ridiculous now, but whenever I had to sit an examination I was terrified I would be asked something I did not know about. The perceived threat of being asked something beyond my knowledge created such fear that I struggled to function, even with material that I was confident about. However, when you think about it rationally, it would be a very cruel examination board that allowed questions to be asked about material that had not been taught. The assessment process is merely a way of demonstrating (showing off) what we have learnt from the taught material. Once I realised that I simply had to use all I had been taught, expanding it with research and applying it in practice, I suddenly had *real* confidence in my written work and began to thoroughly enjoy the assessment process.

New students still look at me strangely when I try to sell assignment writing as a 'fun process' but as the programme unfolds they do begin to understand it and – might I say – even enjoy it. By following the tips in this chapter, students will be able to develop their own confidence in their writing and begin to see assessment as an opportunity and not a huge challenge.

Remember...

for an assignment you will not be asked to write about something that has not been taught. You will be expected to take the taught material and develop it further into an academic piece, using your own research.

Proofreading

Although it sounds like a technical task, you will soon become familiar with proofreading skills, as the proofreading stage is a sign that a piece of work is almost complete. Eventually you will also come to enjoy proofreading your assignments.

It will be useful to manage your time so that you allow two stages for the proofreading process. The first stage involves checking the content, and confirming that you have actually answered the question and met the learning outcomes for that piece of work. A good tip here is to reproduce the assignment brief and any learning outcomes in large print on A4 paper and have them on show throughout your writing and proofreading processes.

The second stage involves checking the spelling, grammar and punctuation. A good guide to basic English grammar and a thesaurus may prove useful. At this stage, you will not be checking the content but the flow and pace of the work, attending to sentence structure as well as spelling and punctuation. A good tip is to read the work aloud; if you get out of breath reading a sentence, then it is too long! Take your time, look at each word individually, and check that the work flows in a logical way. It may be useful to get someone else to help check the spelling and grammar. Note that content cannot be changed by a proofreader because students are required by the university to confirm that the assignment is entirely their own work.

A colleague of mine instructs her students to either PEE or PEA (source unknown) on their work, depending on the level of study. PEE stands for Point, Evidence and Explain and PEA stands for Point, Evidence and Analyse.

- With PEE, each paragraph needs to make a point in the first instance, then evidence should be given to support that point, and then it should be explained.
- With PEA, the point is made, evidence is given and then analysed. Evaluation will then naturally follow in the conclusion of the piece.

Using feedback

Once an assignment has been submitted, many students assume that their work is done. However, particularly in the early days, there is still a long way to go in the development of your assignment-writing skills. The feedback from your assignments should be used effectively. Unfortunately the majority of us take assignment feedback personally, often seeing it as an insult to our ability. Students need to be able to receive constructive criticism in order to develop their skills. It is a natural reaction to feel affronted by feedback because we all feel our written work is the best we can do, yet here is your tutor criticising you. It is not meant to be personal and is not an attack on your skills or knowledge. It is intended to support the development of your skills and knowledge and therefore it should be seen and accepted as another tool for you to use in the planning of your future work. In an ideal world, tutors would give equal amounts of positive feedback and constructive criticism, but as the tutor is intent on developing the skills of the student, the positive side is often reduced in order to support the learning.

Comments made by your tutor may prompt you to extend some areas of your work. They may highlight places where analysis could be incorporated and explain how you can improve your writing. It is easy to take the marked work back, glance at the mark, and then relegate it to your filing system. However, your tutor will have thought long and hard about their comments, with the purpose of encouraging your development. Ideally, you now need to spend some time with the marked piece of work. Read through it, along with the added comments, and try to work out how you could have covered the points made by your tutor. If necessary, make an appointment with your tutor to discuss it further. Verbal feedback should be offered when work is returned. Make use of that one-to-one time. Note down what the tutor tells you, and try to be positive and use this time as the development process it is intended to be. If time allows, it would be useful to re-plan the piece to cover any areas missed, in order to fully appreciate how it could have been written to gain a better result. As a student, you can also reflect on your inner self-talk as described in the next chapter.

Remember...

comments in marked work are not a personal insult. They are intended to encourage further development of your skills.

When I return the first piece of a marked assignment to students on my foundation degree course, I always encourage them to explore how to improve the piece using the feedback I have given them. I encourage them to think about why the comments have been added and how they can develop their work for the next time. A useful activity here is to get them to give some feedback themselves, so I offer them a ridiculously poor piece of work to mark and comment on. Activity 3.1 is one that I devised for foundation degree students at Boston College.

Activity 3.1

Read through the following piece as though you are marking it.

You should be looking at the content, the writing style, spelling and grammar, as well as word-processing and overall presentation. Note down the mistakes and then add comments to help this student improve the piece for re-submission.

lace Knitting

Lace knitting is a art form that has existed for many years. Both men and women can knit. and the skill is often past down from one generation to the next by family members. Knitted lace can make many beautiful things such as capes or shawls for weddings as well as every day cloths. Many babies christening shawls are in lace and they often become family hierlooms that are passed down from one generation to the next. They also make wonderful gifts.Some people used to make a living from knitting things that could be sold. I think Queen victoria had a lace sharwl that was made by one of those people. One man would have many people knitting and he would find the customers. He supplied the wool and he would pay the knitter money for each completed item. They only got a few pennies for each peice though so they had to knit a lot to get a decent income. Lace knitting is a world wide activity and some people can make a good living at it. Designers and writers earn more than the people who do the work. Some celebrites are also famous knitters. Lace knitting produces a fine floating fabric with complicated patterns making the pattern. it can be very difficult to do as it can be hard to follow a pattern to knit lace.

Activity 3.1

There are obviously many mistakes within this piece of writing, far too many to highlight one by one, but here are a few examples to point you in the right direction:

- Use of capital letters: e.g. 'lace' in the title and 'Victoria' in the text.
- Spellings: e.g. cloths should be clothes; babies should be babies'; world wide should be worldwide or world-wide.
- Grammar: 'a art form' should be 'an art form'; use of 'and' to start a sentence (conjunctions such as 'and' and 'but' are best avoided when beginning sentences in academic writing).
- Repetition: e.g. the fact that clothing made in the lace-knitting style is repeated throughout makes the passage tedious.
- Superfluous wording: e.g. celebrities are famous by definition, so why say so in the same sentence (it is unlikely that they are famous for their knitting).
- Sentence structure: e.g. there are several short sentences that state the obvious, such as: 'They also make wonderful gifts.' Although possibly true, this sentence has probably been added without much thought, simply to bulk up the word count.

- Word processing: e.g. the text should be fully justified (fitting to the end of the line on the right side) but you should check your own university guidelines here; spacing between the words is not consistent.

There are many more mistakes, and to list them all would be opening myself to criticism as students point more out more mistakes every time I use the activity. As an expert in healthcare, I will refrain from imagining myself to be an expert in the written word and will rely on students exploring the mistakes using appropriate textbooks to guide them. The exercise then requires students to supply feedback, as in Activity 3.2.

Activity 3.2

Once you have highlighted some mistakes, write out feedback for this student to improve the work.

When you have written the feedback, consider the following:

- How much of the feedback is positive?
- How would you feel if you were the student reading this feedback?
- Can the feedback be written in a more constructive way, giving positives as well as negatives?

After carrying out this activity, foundation degree students realise how difficult it is to give positive feedback, and how easy it is to destroy someone's confidence. They also learn to look for the positives in their own pieces of writing. They appreciate the significance of feedback on their own development and are able to transfer this to working with other students in college and the workplace.

Chapter four
Being Positive

It is an exciting prospect to be starting a new programme of study and for healthcare workers the excitement is often increased by taking on a new role in the workplace. Students either change areas altogether, or take on a new role within their own work area. Whichever route the student takes, the anticipation of new learning, a challenge in the workplace, and the excitement of where this new role may lead, all enable students to commence the programme in a very enthusiastic and optimistic frame of mind.

Commonly, however, after just a few weeks of study, compounded by the demands of a new role in the workplace, students seem to lose the energy that their original enthusiasm generated. Most of my students report experiencing this initial time of high energy, followed by a more difficult period when the impact of study at foundation degree level is felt. If students are prepared for this, then they will study effectively throughout the programme, and make the most of what is in fact a relatively short programme (believe me, two years is not very long at all!).

In any area of our lives we experience highs and lows. Some lows we manage well, learning from, and making the most of them; but some lows drag us down, making us feel disillusioned and demotivated. For the prospective foundation degree student, planning for these highs and lows will help them stay on a more even keel over the two years, and can help reduce the stress that some students experience. Staying positive when the going gets tough is a trick that I learnt while studying for my Certificate in Education at De Montfort University. Having experienced some difficult situations in the classroom, I carried out some action research on what was actually happening. Action research is the process of bringing about a change in practice or policy using methods relevant to the project.

I had realised that the classroom management skills I employed were ineffective. Faced with certain difficulties, I had decided that teaching was not for me and that I could not handle certain situations. I was even looking for another position. However, I used the process of action research to establish where my problems lay and how I could address them. As often happens with action research, the result was quite surprising – the problem was not how I managed my students but how I managed myself! The action research proved that the problem was not an inability to handle difficult situations; it was the way in which I managed myself and how I perceived the situation. I realised that, as soon as something becomes awkward, I have a tendency to berate myself, believing that I cannot manage the situation, when in fact there are many ways to manage difficult situations, which I was fully aware of. It was my 'self-talk' (Rogers, 1992) that was causing the problems.

As Rogers (1992) explains, self-talk is the internal dialogue that we all use consciously or subconsciously. Sometimes called inner speech, it can impact on our emotional well-being and when it follows a negative thread it can be demoralising and demotivating. Self-talk is literally the dialogue that goes on in our heads throughout our lives. We all talk to ourselves inside our heads. We go over our experiences, exploring what went well and what we feel we have not managed so well. We plan events and speeches and prepare ourselves for events by talking ourselves through what might happen. If you tune in to your own self-talk, observe how you perceive yourself in different situations and interactions. We all talk constantly to ourselves, and this dialogue can have a huge impact on our feelings.

We all use self-talk as a matter of course. If things go well, we tell ourselves how pleased we are.

When things go badly we berate ourselves with expressions like:

- I am hopeless.
- I am useless.
- I cannot do this.
- I am an idiot.

All these expressions succeed in doing is to reinforce our sense of failure and reduce our ability to manage difficult situations. When similar situations occur, we immediately enter into a negative mode of thinking and subsequently fail again. By employing positive self-talk, we can reverse this negative spiral and become more positive in our outlook, more proactive in difficult situations and more in control of our own destinies.

Directional language involves changing our damaging negative self-talk into more appreciative, positive and optimistic talk (Rogers, 1992). Our self-talk has been a natural part of us for a very long time and so changing it into more positive, directional language takes practice and time. It may be useful to have a small notebook to keep with you in which you can write positive motivational phrases. You will then be able to refer to it whenever negative self-talk takes hold and this will encourage a more optimistic attitude. For an example, see Box 4.1.

Box 4.1 Negative and positive self-talk

Negative: I always …
Positive: I sometimes – even often – … but …

Negative: I never …
Positive: I can do it when …

Negative: I can't stand it when …
Positive: It may be difficult, but …

As changing our way of being can take a huge amount of concentration and time, it may be easier to 'raise' negative self-talk with a positive afterthought. So when we say to ourselves 'I *never* manage to get this right' we could continue with '… but next time I will' (Rogers, 1992). This will lift our mood, giving us positive feelings and will ultimately lead to a much calmer way of being.

You may find it useful to read the book by Susan Jeffers *Feel the Fear and Do It Anyway*® (1987). Susan Jeffers is an internationally renowned author who specialises in areas of personal growth and relationships. She has written many books on overcoming the barriers that prevent us from moving forward in a 'positive and optimistic way'. Conducting seminars on this theme, Jeffers claims that she already knows her students before they even enter the room. She states: 'They are like the rest of us: all trying to do the best they can and all uncertain about whether they're good enough.' Jeffers argues that we are held back, even repressed, by our fear of not being able to manage a situation, and that our ultimate fear is 'I can't handle it' (Jeffers, 1987). Through this book, Jeffers offers tools and resources in order to change thoughts and create self-confidence to enable us to move through life in a motivated, positive way. Now have a look at Activity 4.1 (see p. 34).

Activity 4.1

Think of a situation that has not gone the way you wanted it to.

It could be that while tidying up, you broke a favourite ornament; or while relaying information in the workplace, you failed to pass on all of it; or while using the computer, you failed to save and lost some work that was needed urgently.

How did you react?

What sort of language did you use in your self-talk?

Write down the terms you would have used.

Now try thinking of how you can change your perception of the situation into a more positive one.

However bad it is, there has to be a positive side to it. We need to embrace our failures in order to learn from them and develop ourselves and our practice further.

Now rewrite those terms in a more positive way.

How could you have perceived what happened in a more positive light?

By using more positive self-talk, we can train ourselves always to see the positive side of events, thus reducing stress levels when similar things occur, and becoming far more relaxed about the difficulties that we all face in life. Maggie's case study (below) shows how I discovered these techniques of self-understanding, and how I used directional language and self-talk to rectify the issues I was facing.

Case Study

Maggie's case study

Following a change in career, Maggie found herself in a classroom in a college of further education, teaching health and social care to a group of (what she perceived to be) very disaffected students. Previously a midwife, Maggie had strong principles and values. Based on her own experiences of education, she expected the students to have similar values to her own. Maggie considered that behaviour such as eating in class, using mobile phones and reading magazines was worthy of disciplinary action. By raising her voice, removing items from students and generally berating them for this behaviour, she expected to get them to conform to her wishes and conduct themselves in a manner she believed to be appropriate for the classroom. The whole time, Maggie's self-talk involved admonishing herself for being unable to control the group:

'I cannot do this.'

'They will not listen to me.'

'I cannot get them to behave.'

'I am useless at this.'

'It's my fault.'

As a result, Maggie became very dissatisfied in her teaching role and the students found themselves in a poor learning environment.

Maggie had been measuring her students' values, beliefs and principles against her own. Her self-talk was negative and assumed that the fault lay with her. It did not allow for the uniqueness of the individual students involved. She assumed commands and orders would bring respect back to the classroom and that the students would obey her, the lecturer, without argument. Once Maggie explored her own value and belief system and that of the students, she discovered that they were miles apart. Students of today do not hold the same values and they have a very different agenda because of changes in society. They have very different perceptions and expectations of the learning environment. When Maggie explored her self-talk she discovered that she was blaming herself for the difficult classroom situation and became very angry with herself for not 'being in control'. This showed itself in the way she spoke to the students and created animosity between her and them. As a result, the students were all left feeling very dissatisfied and unsettled by the interactions.

We all live in a stress-laden society, with constant demands on our time, energy, patience and resources. Life happens all around us, and even for the most cosseted of people, the untoward regularly knocks the best-laid plans aside. From our children missing the school bus to unexpected devastating news regarding the health of a loved one, we face a barrage of potentially stressful events every day of our lives. As a student on the foundation degree programme, stress management is going to be one of the most useful strategies you can develop. Again, a plethora of literature on stress management and positive well-being can be found in bookstores, and the trick is to find the methods that work best for you.

As healthcare workers, too, we encounter stressful situations on a daily basis. An anxious client may lash out at us verbally, or a senior member of staff may berate us for not having performed a certain task. The way we deal with these situations and manage ourselves can have far-reaching consequences for our own emotional well-being and self-esteem. It is often not the fact that we have encountered a stressful situation – it is our perception of it, and how we think about it, that does the damage.

Before studying self-talk and directional language, I used to internalise all the difficult situations I encountered. I would berate myself for being a failure and take all the blame or responsibility for outcomes on myself. Without realising it, this meant that I could not move forward optimistically. I was caught in a downward spiral of self-blame, self-punishment and hesitation in subsequent situations that prevented me from functioning in a truly professional way. By using directional language and positive self-talk, I feel I am now able to manage situations that would previously have caused uncertainty and some distress.

One of my students recounted a traumatic experience from her workplace, as described in the next case study. At that time we were studying reflective practice, using a taught model to reinforce their learning that involved reflecting on an incident from their workplace. After reading about Janet's experience, try Activity 4.2 (opposite).

Case study

Janet's case study

Janet had been caring for a 35-year-old woman who had been diagnosed with terminal cancer. However, the woman died suddenly and unexpectedly from a secondary complication to her condition. This was very traumatic for her husband and her children, aged just 4 and 7 years old, and everyone else involved, including Janet. Janet internalised her own feelings of guilt and responsibility in a very unhealthy way. While recounting the event, for the purpose of a reflective activity, all the emotions Janet had suppressed flowed out. As a mother of an 8-year-old child herself, the self-talk she had used was highly self-blaming:

'There was nothing I could do.'

'I felt so responsible.'

'I should have been able to help them.'

'That poor little boy.'

'I should have been able to save her – her son needed her.'

Activity 4.2

Consider the phrases that Janet used during her self-talk.

How would these phrases impact on her self-esteem and general well-being?

The result for Janet was that she kept those thoughts in her head for months after the event. She reacted badly in similar events, and became very tearful in stressful situations, eventually relating every bad experience to that one situation. Through allowing the negative self-talk to dominate her thoughts and behaviour, Janet became stressed to the point where she eventually needed professional help in the form of counselling.

With an understanding of directional language and positive self-talk in what was a very traumatic situation, Janet may well have been able to see the positives and manage this situation better. I can feel you reacting here and asking what could be positive in this dreadful situation? Ultimately Janet had cared for this woman and her family to the best of her ability. The woman had all her needs met. She was clean, comfortable and pain free. Her family were supported by the medical and nursing staff and they would eventually adapt to the changes. Janet should have been satisfied with performing the tasks to the best of her ability, and pleased with herself for a 'job well done'.

A long time afterwards, Janet was still recounting the event as though it had happened yesterday; it greatly impacted on later events and led to her seeking professional advice herself. Unfortunately, at the time of writing, Janet has only just sought professional help in order to resolve these issues. As healthcare workers, we need to adopt tools to help us manage difficult situations, as once one client leaves our care, another is there, demanding an equal amount of time, attention and strength. As healthcare workers, we need to take care of ourselves as much as we care for our clients.

It may be useful to create your own self-help group, either in your workplace or with peers from your study programme. With a group of people you trust, you can explore how you react in given situations, what your self-talk is saying, and how you can use directional language to increase your self-esteem. It may also be useful to keep that small notebook with positive directional phrases to hand, and use it to promote positive self-talk as events occur. Activity 4.3 focuses more on your self-talk.

Activity 4.3

Observe yourself over the next few weeks, focusing on how you use self-talk when things go well – and also in bad situations.

Note the difference and relate this to how you felt about each event (e.g. any self-talk used and accompanying feelings).

Reflect on the more negative events and try to create some positive phrases that may encourage you to have a more positive attitude towards life's little challenges.

Clearly, directional language and positive self-talk are tools that can be used to promote your own self-esteem and well-being. They do need to be practised until it becomes second nature to use them appropriately – these traits have been a part of our characters for a long time. Self-talk techniques are tools that students can develop in order to support themselves through difficult times, even if they are only used in order to bring about acceptance of what is happening and how it impacts on the individual.

Chapter five
Values for Healthcare Workers

Care work is deeply rooted in the values and ethics of all concerned. As healthcare workers, we need to understand not only our own values but also those of our co-workers and of course our clients. We give care by meeting the physical, intellectual, emotional and social needs of our clients (see Chapter 6). Yet we need to recognise each of our clients as unique people, with different values, each requiring an individual approach to their particular situation. So even if we are working on a ward full of clients with very similar health conditions (fractured limbs, for example), they will all have very different needs according to their specific values, beliefs and situations. In modern healthcare settings the emphasis of any care lies within a necessary quality domain with quality being at the forefront of our practice. Unfortunately, quality requirements can obscure the importance of our own values and beliefs and of those we care for, resulting in a loss of the sensitivity which ought to dominate our actions.

All healthcare workers are guided by the Care Value Base mentioned by Moonie, Nolan and Lavers (Moonie *et al.*, 2003). This provides the foundation for the expected behaviour of healthcare workers. All healthcare professionals should foster people's rights and responsibilities and their equality and diversity, and maintain their confidentiality (Moonie *et al.*, 2003). The overlap between these three desirable behaviours is shown in Fig. 5.1 (see p. 40).

All people have the right to freedom, the right to be different, and the right to choice, dignity, safety and security. Our clients need respect and recognition of boundaries, particularly those concerning roles. They require resources to meet health and social care needs, effective communication and the reassurance that healthcare workers will challenge situations in which these needs and rights are not met. They must understand prejudice, stereotyping, labelling, assumptions and oppression, with an acceptance of the diversity of all by everyone involved in care work (Moonie *et al.*, 2003).

All these factors contribute to the professional qualities of healthcare workers and are the backbone of all relationships within the healthcare arena. In order to be truly effective, care workers need to be fully aware of their own values and beliefs. They need to appreciate how their own values and beliefs have developed, and acknowledge the influences that may affect them. Values are ideals, beliefs, customs and characteristics that individuals, groups or society as a whole find valuable, acceptable and worthwhile (Hendrick, 2004).

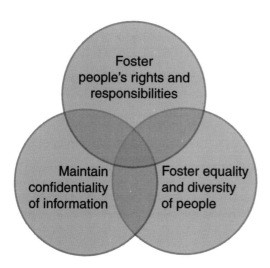

Fig. 5.1: *The three main behaviours embraced by the Care Value Base* (adapted from Moonie *et al.*, 2003).

Values develop in the individual over their lifetime. Some values remain constant, while others may change and develop, depending on individual life circumstances and experiences. Values are influenced by our culture, education, environment, employment, family life, religion and life experience (Hendrick, 2004). These aspects may change many times in our lives so we need a full awareness of how values are affected by our lifestyle and experience. Using reflective practice to fully understand ourselves, and making it a regularly repeated activity, can enable us to acknowledge change and keep that all-important understanding of individuality.

As healthcare workers, we are also expected to consider the values of the workplace, especially those contained within the various codes of practice that exist in the NHS today. Professional values need to be recognised by students as an intrinsic part of their professional lives, which will change and develop depending on their own circumstances and experiences, but they always need to be at the forefront of everyday working life. At the moment the roles of trainee assistant practitioners and assistant practitioners are not governed by an official body, meaning that there is no statutory code of conduct to regulate them. It is only a matter of time before the assistant practitioner becomes registered with a governing body and supported by guidelines associated with that body. Individual health trusts may be developing their own codes of conduct as a guide to support the practice of trainee assistant practitioners and assistant practitioners.

How do we learn our values?

Our values are initially taught by our parents or primary carers, with teachers and other responsible adults encouraging their development throughout our compulsory education. They can be influenced by our peers, by wider family members and by other people whom we meet during our formative years. For instance, if we have a role model, someone we greatly admire and look up to, we may subconsciously take on their values as our own. Entering the work environment opens our experience to different values, particularly if we enter a professional environment such as healthcare. We then take on the professional codes of conduct (values) promoted by the professional bodies concerned. Individual values are an ever-changing concept. We need to develop an awareness of our own values, how they have developed over time and how they will continue to develop and change as we live through different life experiences. As professional healthcare workers, we need to be continually aware of these values in ourselves and others, accepting them as intrinsic to human nature, and understanding how they can affect behaviour.

In reading around the subjects of values and ethics, students learn the meanings of the many terms used. It is beyond the scope of this book to fully explore them, but a list is given in Box 5.1. It may be useful to explore the meaning of these words before starting the foundation degree programme.

Box 5.1 Values and ethics terminology

- **Assumptions**
- **Autonomy**
- **Beneficence**
- **Diversity**
- **Equality**
- **Integrity**
- **Justice**
- **Labelling**
- **Non-maleficence**
- **Oppression**
- **Stereotyping**
- **Value**

By the time someone becomes a trainee assistant practitioner, they will have made millions of ethical decisions in their personal and professional lives. These decisions will have been based on their own values, moral virtues and ethical principles as well as the professional code of the workplace. All these elements should be taught in the foundation degree programme. Students are also expected to have an awareness of their own values and an understanding of how to make the ethical decisions required in everyday healthcare practice.

This chapter aims to help students to explore their own values and those of others around them. It aims to encourage thought about the different ethical decisions we make every day, and to build a greater understanding of the relationship between carers and those who are cared for, between carers and co-workers, and possibly a greater understanding of carers' own personal relationships.

On a daily basis, healthcare workers make decisions that are laden with values and have ethical implications for all concerned – the carers, the cared for, and other connected people. Understanding our own values can only aid these decision-making processes and ensure that we are always aware of the individual values of other people. Use Activity 5.1 to explore your own values.

Activity 5.1

Make a list of what you believe to be your basic values.

It will probably include things like honesty, truthfulness, compassion, integrity and dignity. Then give a brief definition of each of the words that you have chosen to describe your own values.

Check your definitions against the definitions given in a dictionary or an ethics textbook.

How different is your interpretation?

Would you now change your choice of words?

If possible, ask one of your colleagues from your workplace to do the same activity and compare your responses. Is there much difference between them? Why might these differences occur?

Consider how different your values and beliefs as a carer may be from those of a client.

They might be very different, but would this affect the care you give?

A difference in values may not affect the actual care given, but may affect how communication is interpreted and the relationship of the caregiver with the client, and ultimately the acceptance and experience of care for that client. These are all things that ought to be considered by healthcare workers in modern healthcare settings, as illustrated by Activity 5.2 (see p. 44).

Activity 5.2

Imagine that you are an elderly client, in a side room on a busy ward.

You are quite frail and unable to get out of your chair or bed alone. You have very few visitors. You feel very unwell but are uncertain as to what the problem is and whether it can be rectified easily.

List the values that you would like the healthcare workers caring for you to have.

Why would you want your carers to have those specific values?

Would carers with those listed values be able to meet your every need?

Once we understand our own values and appreciate those of others, particularly those of the people we care for, we can practise healthcare in an ethical way. Understanding our own values will influence our behaviour by providing a framework that enables us to make decisions, and understand new situations and relationships. Alongside reflective practice, this will guide you through experiences, helping you develop into accountable, decisive, autonomous and reflective practitioners.

Ethics

> *'Good ethics is comprehensive deliberation about the pros and cons of action.'*
> Seedhouse, 2009

In the course of writing this book I was honoured to be given permission to use some of the work of David Seedhouse, a renowned author of material on health and medical ethics. Seedhouse clearly states in the third edition of his book, *Ethics: The Heart of Health Care,* that ethics is not an 'add-on alternative' which we either consider or leave well alone; rather it is 'the heart' of healthcare and healthcare workers (Seedhouse, 2009). It is to be embraced and cherished in our working lives and not left to others to worry about.

Seedhouse also states that 'healthcare is fundamentally a moral task'. He uses a case study of his own experience on consultation with an ear, nose and throat (ENT) specialist. This clearly demonstrates a situation that is (in my opinion) far too common in healthcare environments today. The case study is reproduced later (see Chapter 7) and for the purpose of this book it is intended to encourage a consideration of ethics and values, relationships and hierarchies, and good and poor practice.

To summarise the story, Seedhouse consulted an ENT specialist after feeling a lump in his salivary gland. There was poor practice in his case. Assumptions were made by the healthcare workers, which resulted in a bad experience that could have had a far-reaching impact on his mental well-being. Assumptions were specifically made regarding his understanding of the whole process and his understanding of the condition. Reassurances were only given in a half-hearted manner and assumptions made that they were appropriate. An attitude approaching indifference was adopted, possibly with the intention of removing anxiety, but which actually caused his anxiety to increase greatly. How many times in our professional working lives have we perpetrated or witnessed similar incidents? It is an assumption on our part that telling a client not to worry means they will not worry. No one can forget about an unsettling health scare – even temporarily.

Incidents such as Seedhouse's experience evoke memories of a bygone day when healthcare firmly followed the Biomedical Model of Health, with doctors as white-coated oracles whom no one defied. In those days, nurses were the handmaidens of the doctors. They did as they were told in a way prescribed by the doctors, and clients were totally subservient. Fortunately, the world of healthcare has changed dramatically. Today there is a wholly holistic approach to care, with multidisciplinary teams of carers, and clients who have more knowledge about their conditions than ever before. Nurses and healthcare workers have a greater understanding of the care that is being given and qualified healthcare workers are much more autonomous in their own practice.

For nurses and healthcare workers, this seems to have brought about a three-fold role. They support the care given by the doctor; they practise in their own right; and they are advocates for the client. Of course they need to know the client well enough to be a true advocate, but do we ever know anyone well enough to be able to determine what situations they can manage, which ones will cause stress, and how they will react to unexpected news? In defence of healthcare workers, I would say that we can never have that amount of knowledge about someone – and yet to give truly ethical care, we ought to.

As not one of us can have the absolute knowledge to support all the clients we meet on a daily basis, we need to take steps to offer the most appropriate care in the most appropriate way. Our training and continuous professional development ensures that we practise in an evidence-based way, following the policies and procedures of the workplace. As individuals, we can develop our knowledge and understanding of values and ethics in order to give truly equitable care to all our clients. Understanding values and ethics is not a stand-alone activity. It needs to be constantly reflected on, constantly considered, and kept at the forefront of our everyday work practice.

Chapter six
Health Matters

Common words in healthcare can often have very ambiguous meanings. One word can mean very different things to different people, particularly because there is so much diversity among healthcare professionals and clients (who are mostly lay people). Activity 6.1 explores this further. In order to give care to benefit health, we need to be aware of what these ambiguous words mean, for us and for those we care for.

Activity 6.1

Write out a brief definition of each of the following words, outlining what they mean to you as an individual:

- **Health**
- **Care**
- **Fitness**
- **Ability.**

The word 'health' has a definite meaning for the professional healthcare worker. It is assumed that we all accept this definition and it is assumed that we understand the impact of this definition on every person. The professional concept of health was defined by the World Health Organization in 1948 as 'a state of complete physical, mental and social well-being and not merely the absence of disease or infirmity'. This definition has been contested over the years, with some people arguing that the words 'complete' and 'absence' are too restrictive to encompass the reality for everyone.

The 1986 Ottawa Charter for Health Promotion developed another definition for health, whereby health is 'a resource for everyday life, not the object of living. Health is a positive concept that emphasises social and personal resources as well as physical capabilities.' This definition tends towards the wider environmental and social aspects that make up an individual's situation within which their health is determined. However, it still fails to incorporate people's individuality and the impact of personal values and beliefs that would have a strong influence on an individual's definition of health.

We have to accept that health is a difficult concept to define and that it will most certainly mean very different things to the different people we meet in our working lives. We need to develop a respect for these differences and care for individuals equitably. Activity 6.2 looks at the meaning of the word 'health' in more detail.

Activity 6.2

Ask a few different people to give you their definition of the word health.

Select people from a health-related professional area as well as some lay people (with no healthcare training whatsoever).

Compare the answers given by the two groups.

Note that lay definitions of health may include:

'Being fit enough to partake in strenuous activity.'

'Being able to get up in the morning.'

'Freedom from disease.'

'Being able to manage a disease with little or no interruption to daily life.'

'Being happy.'

The word 'care' can also have different meanings and is often used in quite a careless way. We complete a phone call by saying 'take care' and we instruct each other to 'take care' when driving or going about our business. We talk of children being 'in care' and regularly read 'care' labels while doing our laundry. The underlying theme is to be careful, be safe and not to take any risks, although quite the opposite can actually be true. Often, when we use the word 'care' we are actually protecting ourselves! We ask our children to 'take care' while they walk to school, but the bottom line is that we cannot imagine dealing with the outcome should an accident occur. Care can be a very selfish word that may involve protecting ourselves, even when it seems to be the opposite.

Exploring the word 'fitness' can also create another dilemma for healthcare professionals. Fitness to some is the ability to perform high levels of strenuous sport such as running a marathon, and yet to others it may be having the ability to get up in the morning and make a cup of tea. We all measure our definitions within our individual abilities and within certain constraints of health and disease, meaning that a person with a chronic debilitating disease may actually consider themselves quite 'fit'. We need to develop an understanding of how others may define these terms in order to truly understand conversations using these ambiguous words.

Use of specialised language

Every profession uses a specific language that can be bewildering to people outside that discipline. As healthcare professionals, we are particularly prone to this, using acronyms on a daily basis, without due consideration for our clients who have little understanding of their meaning.

When I first met my husband, he worked in the aviation industry. He used to talk about inspecting 'STDs', which is a term that health professionals would instantly recognise as meaning 'sexually transmitted diseases'. I was very confused about what he might be doing in his workplace. Finally I asked him for a definition. In his field, STD meant 'synthetic training device' and this is a good example of how specific industry-related language can cause a lot of confusion. Within the healthcare profession, this may cause distress to vulnerable clients, creating further anxiety for already stressed people. Activity 6.3 explores how acronyms are used in different situations.

Activity 6.3

Take a few minutes to recall some of the abbreviated terms you use in your daily working life.

Then consider *where* you use them (in the workplace, at home, or maybe socially) and *why* you use them.

Activity 6.3

Using the specialised language associated with a specific profession makes us feel as though we are part of that group. It makes us feel that we have inclusivity in a special area of our lives, which boosts our self-esteem and confidence with other people in that group. Unfortunately the inclusivity we gain from this also creates a sense of exclusion – amongst people who do not understand our language. It can intimidate them and cause confusion and more importantly it can raise anxiety in people who in reality need to be given confidence by our words and actions. Activity 6.4 looks at the use of jargon in the healthcare environment.

Activity 6.4

Next time you are in the workplace look out for other staff members using professional jargon.

- When do they use it?
- With whom do they use it?
- To what effect do they use it?

For many of the people we meet during a usual working day, being cared for is a unique experience. It is out of the ordinary for them, and they can be quite bewildered and intimidated by it. If we are feeling frail, fragile and anxious, the last thing we want is to be worried further by the language or words that are used in our presence.

Models of health

As stated previously, the intention of this book is not to teach theory but to encourage you to think about the study you are undertaking. Through participating in the foundation degree programme, you will learn about various models of health that exist in healthcare practice today. While teaching at Boston College, I taught students the models and frameworks that are used in care practice, without duly considering the understanding I was giving. It was only recently that I realised that these students never truly understood the basics of these structures that we refer to so readily.

When studying healthcare matters, we use frameworks and models to develop understanding in order to give care. The structures are accepted as the basis for care work, but it is assumed that the students appreciate the organisation of the information.

A framework is just that – a structure to support understanding; a way of directing thought processes correctly. Imagine a framework as an unadorned coat-stand. It may have several arms on which we are directed to hang coats – or certain attributes. Consider the 'umbrella' presentation of the Health and Safety at Work Act 1974. Within its umbrella shape, there are five general headings that cover all the aspects of health and safety. The headings direct us to the areas we might need in any given situation, perhaps regarding the notification of infectious diseases, or manual handling of equipment, or first aid matters, and each is supported by one arm of the framework of the whole Act.

A model, on the other hand, is a more generalised depiction of the overall subject. A model of health could also be represented by a coat-stand, but each arm will have a specific significance. It is a coat-stand with clothes on. The Social Model of Health, for example, has six distinct arms – physical health, mental health, emotional health, social health, spiritual health and societal health – to which any one client's situation may be related. One client's situation would not necessarily relate to every arm, but would require consideration of some of them. As a healthcare worker, you would use the model in a way suited to each client. Naturally, no two clients would fit the model in the same way.

The Biopsychosocial Model of Health would thus be a very complex 'coat-stand'. The main arm of the stand would be one person, and it would branch out with many extended arms in a complex web that covers every possible aspect of the person, and the interconnections between the different aspects. Again it would direct healthcare workers to the myriad possibilities to be considered in the care of that person.

Theory

Theory is developed through research, in which an idea is explored using appropriate methods until it is proved one way or the other. The idea (hypothesis) is explored through experimentation (research) on a group of people (sample group) in order to prove whether it is true or not. If repeatedly proven to be true in a valid way, then the hypothesis can become a theory. Theory often supports understanding, as in the development of models and frameworks. A model is a guide to be used to direct the care given. It enables policies to be implemented and procedures to be developed in order to cover all aspects of the care that may be needed. As time passes, different perspectives can be taken into account and the model changed to suit the ever-changing needs of the discipline.

A good example here is the history surrounding models of health. Some 50 years ago, all healthcare was predominantly managed according to the Biomedical Model of Health. This model was based on scientific experimentation, whereby the doctor was seen as the medical practitioner in charge of all health issues. The human body was seen as a machine, with parts being repaired as needed – rarely considering the whole person. The client (or, in those days, the patient) was passive, accepting that the medical world repaired those parts of the body that were damaged, before being sent on their way, fit enough to return to active life. Illness and disease were seen as failings of the body that could either be repaired or not, and the emphasis was on repair and 'make do', with the responsibility for the outcome falling almost entirely on the medical profession.

Some time later, the debate about wider external influences moved healthcare towards the more holistic Social Model of Health. This model included the impact of the environment in which we live affecting the health of the individual; it shifted the weight of responsibility more towards the client, as well as the medical staff. The Social Model of Health considered all the determinants that influence health, such as age, gender, demography, employment and education. It enabled wider thinking about the causes of ill health and disease, and gave scope for these wider influences to feature in the treatment of some conditions (for instance, by recommending that people being treated for respiratory conditions should avoid damp environments).

Recently the models of health have been revised again and healthcare is now centred on the Biopsychosocial Model, incorporating genetic factors, pathogens, thought processes and environments in the equation. It would be useful for prospective students to read more about these models to gain further understanding of the basic theoretical grounding of care practice in the UK. These models – along with the Care Value Base (Moonie *et al.*, 2003) described in Chapter 5 – underpin the understanding of anyone working in healthcare today.

Health beliefs

Health beliefs are particular to each and every one of us. Some people have strong health beliefs connected to their upbringing or religion, while others barely consider them. Our own health beliefs are the part of us that lies behind our health choices. Some people with strong positive health beliefs always choose healthy options and take few risks. Others have a more fatalistic attitude; they might ignore health advice because the outcome may not affect them, taking a head-in-the-sand attitude of 'it will not happen to me'.

Closely linked to our values (Chapter 5), health beliefs are an intrinsic part of our characters. They can be changed, but it takes a lot of effort on our part. What needs to be remembered here is that we should work in an equitable way, not blaming people for the health choices they make but supporting them to the best of our ability and in a fair and non-discriminatory way. For healthcare workers in the fields of public health and health promotion, this creates a veritable minefield – aiming to encourage healthy choices but unable to cater for every health belief they meet. We can give education and advice, in the most appropriate way possible, but the choices are down to the individual person, who needs to be respected as an individual.

Factors that impact on health

Along with health beliefs and definitions of health, we also need to be aware of the factors that can impact on the health of people, and of course their health choices. Again, much has been written on this subject, and it would be advisable to read some of the published material. Dahlgren and Whitehead's model is a useful starting point, because it gives the full range of factors, from individual lifestyle choices to much wider general social and cultural issues (cited in Sussex *et al.*, 2008).

It is vital to be aware of how an individual's background can affect the health choices they make. We often make suggestions to improve health that are way beyond that person's ability to follow. This creates an unbalanced relationship between the professional and the client that can have longstanding implications for the future health care of that client.

The content of this chapter is closely related to that of Chapter 5. There are few subjects in health and social care that are stand-alone. Most topics are interwoven, and have many outside influences. The healthcare worker needs to develop an awareness of all these issues in order to provide care in a truly equitable fashion.

Attributes of a healthcare worker

Here is a selection of words and phrases that may be used to describe a healthcare worker. Read through them, consider each one as a desirable attribute, and think about which of them you already recognise in yourself and which you would like to aspire to.

Loyal · Caring · Trustworthy · Honest · Fair · Open · Kind · Punctual
Tidy · Non-judgemental · Diplomatic · Not prone to stereotype others
Respectful · Confident · Knowledgeable · Safe · Strong · Patient

Strong sense of self · Efficient · Effective · Team player · Good personal hygiene · Good communication skills (verbal and non-verbal) · Sensible Reliable · Committed · Truthful

This list could go on and on. As it stands, it demonstrates that we, as care-workers, are complex people, coming from a variety of backgrounds with many external influences and a wide range of skills and abilities. Our clients are the same – a very diverse group of people, with countless factors impacting on them. In order to give care, we need to appreciate our selves and our ability to care, be aware of our own limitations and accept that each individual client we meet is an equally complex person. We can never assume we know enough about ourselves and/or the people we care for. The individual is an ever-changing concept that we need to continually reflect on and study in order to be able to perform in a truly professional manner.

Activity 6.5

Make a list of the attributes that you believe a healthcare worker should demonstrate.

Think about Chapter 5 again. How does your list of attributes match the values you named in yourself and those that the client may have required?

Chapter seven
Food for Thought

This chapter is based on a case study. It pulls together threads from various other chapters and encourages you, as the student, to think about the care that we give, as healthcare workers. The case study is quite long and it depicts an isolated experience in healthcare of an otherwise healthy man, David Seedhouse, who has given kind permission for me to reproduce it here. It relates his experience with an ear, nose and throat (ENT) surgeon in his home town in New Zealand. Even though his healthcare experience is not of British origin, I believe it reflects a type of experience that is not uncommon in British hospitals. I am sure many of you would be able to recount similar events that you or your colleagues have witnessed. As professional healthcare workers, we need to develop an awareness that all our actions have consequences – that we believe we are acting in a professional manner but things may be perceived quite differently by our clients.

David Seedhouse published this case study in the third edition of his book *Ethics: The Heart of Health Care* (2009) as an example of ethical considerations. You may find it useful to revisit, once you have studied the ethics module of your foundation degree programme. Here I am using the case study not only for ethical consideration but also to explore health beliefs and values, and to get an overall glimpse of the perceptions of both professionals and the client.

I would encourage you to read through the case study several times before looking at the questions and statements that follow. I am not trying to be devil's advocate here, but rather want to encourage you to think of how care may be perceived. This way, I hope you will develop an awareness that will improve your practice and that of others. The superscript numbers will direct you to the areas I would like you to consider later.

Case Study

David Seedhouse's case study

This is an account of the personal experience of David Seedhouse. It is reproduced in its entirety with kind permission of Wiley-Blackwell from D. Seedhouse (2009) *Ethics: The Heart of Health Care*, 3rd edn, pp. iii-vii.

For as long as I can recall I had a small, firm, roundish, mobile lump below and slightly forward of my left ear.[1] I didn't worry about it, just fiddled with it occasionally as I shaved (it seemed insignificant and stayed the same size). I mostly forgot it completely. Sometime before Christmas 1996, I noticed it again. It seemed a little bigger, but I couldn't be sure. In any case I couldn't imagine it would be serious. I'm healthy and expect to stay that way, after all.

In early December I went to the GP for a couple of things and mentioned it to her.[2] I could tell, from her immediate distraction, that it might be serious. Instantly I began to feel sick (sick to the stomach and sick that I was in trouble and sickest that this might affect Hilary – my wife – and Charlotte – my daughter). The GP, who seemed to have an intuitive understanding of the relationship between ethics and work for health, was straight and to the point: 'You'll need to see an ENT surgeon. You may need an operation. Do you have medical insurance? No? Well it may cost two to three thousand dollars so we'll try the public system first.'

I stuttered some questions, mostly to establish just how much I should worry. She said: 'I'm 99.9 percent certain that it isn't cancer.[3] I know what a cancer feels like. I used to work in a hospice.'

> *'Should I worry about this?'*

> 'No.'

But I did, of course. Dazedly, with the help of Hilary's characteristically perceptive prompting, I wondered. If it's nothing to worry about, why do I need to see the ENT surgeon? What exactly is this problem? And later that evening, if it is going to cost three thousand dollars then what will the operation involve?

I managed to put the problem to the back of my mind for at least some of the time and got on as best I could.[4] Just before a brief holiday in Nelson I received an outpatient appointment to Auckland hospital, which made trepidation unavoidable.

I went to the hospital *worried and ignorant*.[5] I emphasise this because – though

I'm probably over anxious – I imagine the great majority of patients in similar situations must feel as I did, and I emphasise it because it must surely be obvious to anyone seeing people in such circumstances that this is how they must be feeling.

After a wait of three-quarters of an hour, in a crowded waiting room, unable to establish how long I would have to wait despite politely asking the receptionist, I was shown into a consulting room by a nurse. Will I get my lump cut out here and now? I thought. I hoped so. I hoped it would be a local anaesthetic and that would be that, but I was forlorn to see a small room, not surgically equipped. I knew already that my worrying would have to go on.

The doctor wasn't there and the nurse was trying to be cheerful – I can't remember what she said but she seemed more nervous than I.[6] She scurried around like a giant mouse. She was about to rush away with my notes when I managed to ask if I could see them. 'Of course' she said, 'these days you have a right to,' but she was in so much of a hurry I could read no more than the GP's referral letter which asked for the surgeon's opinion on excision, with the brief history I had given. Thoughtfully my GP had highlighted in pink the sentence: *The patient is senior lecturer in medical ethics at the medical school.*

The surgeon, a conspicuously overweight middle-aged man, breezed in. I stood up – I think he may have held out his hand to introduce himself. He immediately said, 'Where's this lump then?' and felt it as he wished.[7]

Almost instantly, or so it seemed to me, he announced, 'You have a benign tumour of the salivary gland' (I didn't know if I was relieved or shocked – I certainly had no idea what this meant). He then directed me toward the examining table and told me to lie down. 'I just want to take a needle biopsy' (I think that was what he said).

He didn't ask for permission, and he didn't say there might be untoward consequences (other than the obvious one of finding out that I had cancer), and I was obedient. It all happened so quickly it is hard to see how I could have objected without causing considerable fuss. He took his needle and inserted it into my lump.

'This might hurt a bit.'

'*Yes.*'

What else do you say? It did hurt a bit – not much, though it hurt more when he wiggled the needle round inside the lump.

As he was doing this he was speaking. Something along the lines of:

'So you're a lecturer in ethics are you? Where?'

'At the medical school, across the road.'

'I've not seen you before.'

'I don't see many surgeons.' (This was an attempt at a joke. It went unnoticed.)

'I don't bother with the medical school anymore – too socialist for me.'

'Oh no,' I said, looking at the nurse out of my left eye, between the needle and the surgeon's arms. She raised her eyebrows. In sympathy, I think.

He squirted the sample between two microscope slides. As he did he called his registrar in.

'This is Dr Blah Blah.'

'Hello.'

'This patient has blah blah blah.'

What did he say? Before I had time to ask, registrar Blah Blah said, 'That's all I need to know,' and left the room.

'Thanks, Doc,' I managed.

I was told to sit up and return to the doctor's desk. I felt shakier than ever.

'You need an operation, but there is a risk.'

'Ok,' I said.

What!? I thought. He showed me what needed to be done. He reached under his left ear and with his right hand made as if to pull back a large flap of skin, just as a cartoon character would remove a mask.

'It is not easy to get at the blah blah. There is a less than 1% chance of damage to the facial nerve. Even if all goes well you'll have a sore ear and your ear lobe will almost certainly always be numb.'

I couldn't believe this. This wasn't happening.

'What's the worst that can happen?'

I was convinced he was going to say 'You'll die.' But he said nothing. Instead he took his finger and pulled the left side of his mouth firmly downwards.

'Oh God,' I thought. I knew I wasn't right but I hadn't expected this.

After I told him I hadn't insurance he put me on the waiting list for the public hospital.

'How long will I wait for?'

'I can't say, you know what a mess the public system is at the moment – it could be months.'

'Does that matter?'

'No, but the tumour needs to be removed.'

Without meaning to, he then reassured me.

'I won't ask you to wait for the result of the biopsy because I'm virtually certain what it is.'

'When will I know for sure?'

'If you don't hear within a week, it is what I think it is.'

At some point – whether before or after this I can't recall – he said, 'Of course, if you went private it could be done much quicker – I have a private practice but I'm not supposed to tell you that here.'

'How much?'

'It could be four and a half thousand.'

'You'd better give me your card.'

'I don't have a card here, but here is the number of my private rooms.'

There were several questions floating in my mind – and I wasn't so thrown I'd forgotten what these were – but he was pointedly waiting to leave so I only managed to put a couple – and these had to be prompts to him.

'So, if I don't have this removed it gets bigger and then can cause damage?'

'Yes.'

'You think I should get this done?'

'Yes.'

And that was that. I gave my form to the receptionist and reeled out of the ward, unable to think straight, with months of anxiety ahead. I went to my office across the street and called Hilary.[8] She was shocked and upset but had the presence of mind to advise me to call my friend, a retired physician. I told him I had a benign tumour (I hoped) of the parotid gland (though that wasn't what the doctor had said to the registrar, I was sure). Because I work in a medical school I have access to the library so I read up what I could. I wasn't sure what sort of tumour I had (I discovered there are different sorts of benign parotid tumour) but my friend – on further inquiry – told me he thought it was most likely a mixed cell tumour, and if so, it should come out because though they grow slowly they don't stop – one book had a picture of a man with one the size of a football – and they can suddenly become malignant (which was worse news than ever, but I was so emotionally deadened by now it didn't matter very much).

I told Hilary and we decided to pay for the operation out of our savings. I called the surgeon at his private rooms. After a couple of hours he called back (to his credit he didn't then know I wanted a private operation). I told him I had decided to pay and asked when he could do it.

'I'm going on holiday soon but I could do you on Tuesday if you like.' (It was Thursday at 4 pm.)

'Ok,' I said, my thoughts muffled in a nightmare.

I pulled out of it, and discovered more about parotid tumours from an internet site. This helped explain the doctor's reasoning (my symptoms fitted a pattern typical of a benign tumour). Two days later I had cause to read the site more carefully still.

A cricket test

On the Saturday, aware I was over-anxious about what might happen, I took myself off to the New Zealand vs England cricket test at Eden Park in Auckland. But though the sunshine baked me I felt bleak, and couldn't concentrate. For no particular reason I decided to move to a seat in the West Stand. As I walked behind the South Stand to get there I was shattered – utterly shattered – to realise that my mouth had filled with blood. I spat it out, oblivious of the spectacle I might make to other people milling around, but the blood kept coming. Swallowing most of it, I went to the Gents for water. I swilled my mouth and saw in the mirror that the lining of my cheek – behind the tumour – seemed to have irregular lines of blood leaking from it.

I felt as if I wasn't there. That's it, I thought. I've had it now. It's cancer and I'm going to die, and at that point I again had the feeling it didn't matter. My – presumably irrational – reaction was if that's it that's it and there's nothing I can do now. [9]

But the blood stopped. It went as quickly as it came. White-faced I bought a diet drink (I had been intending to do this anyway) and walked as if weightless to the West

Stand, where I sat in disbelief. No more blood though.

I couldn't sit at the cricket – so I drove to work (a mile away) to phone Hilary. I didn't want to, but had to tell her what had happened and we were both upset. I was on the verge of tears, but the bleeding had stopped so I rallied. I called the doctor's mobile phone but it was switched off. I called his rooms (no answer – it was Saturday). I called the hospital – maybe Dr Blah Blah, the registrar, can tell me what it is. I got through to him and explained what had happened. He was quite unconcerned. I think this was actually lack of interest but I interpreted it favourably and – as I had done with the surgeon – prompted an answer which had only just occurred to me.[10]

'I assume – I hope – that the blood is something to do with the needle biopsy?'

'Yes,' he said casually, 'there are many small ducts which lead to the inside of the mouth. The surgeon must have damaged some, and they must then have clotted. The clot dissolved, that's all. It's nothing to worry about.'

'It's nothing to worry about if you know what it is,' I said, with surprising force considering my mental state. But he didn't rise to the bait and said – once I told him I had opted for the private operation: 'I'm sure you'll be alright once my boss has operated. As my grandfather used to say, "a stitch in time saves nine."'

Good grief, I couldn't help thinking, he'll be telling me a spoonful of frigging sugar helps the medicine go down next, but I left it. *'Thanks, Doc,'* I said to him for the second time.

I checked on the internet site. Sure enough, here were the risks of needle biopsy, none of which the doctor told me before he took the sample. They are:

Advantages
- Safe, economical, easy to perform, minimal pain.
- Often provides a preoperative diagnosis and may obviate the need for surgery in some patients.

Potential problems
- Haemorrhage
- Fistula formation
- Facial nerve injury
- Infection
- Needle tract implantation
- Interpretation difficulties.

Thanks, Doc, I thought.

At the hospital

The ethically barren pattern continued at the hospital, and I confess I found it difficult to cope. It is important to appreciate how I was feeling – a doctor's moral incompetence always has a human context.[11]

I didn't sleep much the night before my operation, partly because I had to be at the hospital by 7am, and I never sleep well if I know I have to wake before 5. But I got through the night and cycled (yes, cycled) the 14 kilometres to the Medical School.

The morning was dark and warm. I had a tail wind and hardly a car went by. Despite my fears it was impossible not to feel some comfort in the sub-tropical tranquillity that cradled me.

As I walked to the hospital – a private one 20 minutes away – I began to be upset. I was plain scared of what was to come – the pain, the risk and the unconsciousness. But more than this I despaired at my powerlessness – I had opted to place myself in a situation where I knew nothing and could do nothing. I found this paradox frustrating but still I walked toward it, forcing tears away.[12]

I arrived and sat in the foyer waiting to be admitted, observing three other equally miserable new patients with sympathy – and horror that I was one too.[13]

I was shown to my room by a nurse auxiliary. What I saw drove home further (as if I needed it) that despite the floral bedsheets, neat TV and new carpet, I was not booking into a hotel. They were going to cut me open soon and I would be on this bed later, bleeding and hurting.

On the wall by the bed was a bag containing plastic tubes for breathing, a panel of switches with an 'emergency aid' button, and a bag holding a LifeAid™ resuscitator. Standard issue daily apparatus, trivial to a doctor or a nurse, but its presence paralysed me. How can I be here? They don't have resuscitators in hotels. There is nothing I can do now. It was agonising to lose independence so quickly and casually.

A nurse, Charleen, checked me in perfunctorily.[14] I must have sounded scared but she was either unwilling or unable to offer me the reassurances I needed, despite my asking her as many open questions as I could think of: 'Is he a good surgeon?' 'What sort of anaesthetic will it be?' (I wanted her to say, 'Oh, a 100% safe one, you'll love it'), 'How many ops does he do at this hospital?'

As we were completing the consent forms the surgeon entered. I stood up and made as if to shake hands, a gesture he either did not recognise or chose to ignore. 'Have you still got the lump?' he asked, presumably in jest.[15] 'You know I have,' I replied half in annoyance and half bemused. He then took out his purple marker, drew a ring around the lump and started to leave.

'*Is that it?*' I spluttered incredulously.

He stopped. He was slowed anyway by the tight squeeze between Charleen and the wall of my room. Charleen also looked at him, unintentionally forcing him to take a step back toward me. I moved back too, so I could face him squarely.

I can't remember if he said anything. I think he probably didn't. But I know I managed to say – straight out, and again with a courage that surprised me, '*What about the biopsy? What was the result of the biopsy?*' I can't recall the exact words but he indicated, brusquely, that it was OK.

'*So it was a pleomorphic adenoma?*'

'Yes.'

'*So I don't have cancer?*'

'No.'

'*Well that's something good at least.*'

And at that he left, with a flabby wave and a 'Catch you later'.

* * *

Having read the case study, take your time to work through the following questions. They are numbered according to the superscript numbers in the case study itself, so that you can easily refer to the relevant parts, and they are intended to provoke further thought in your responses.

The purpose here is to encourage reflection on actions, understand how care may be perceived, and to develop practice that we hope will prevent these types of encounters from occurring. It is intended to extend your consideration of health beliefs and individual values and to understand how these can impact on behaviour and perceptions of others' behaviour within a care environment. It may be appropriate at times to revisit relevant chapters in this book, or to do some further research in order to explore the issues fully. Please record your thoughts and responses before reading through my comments.

1. What personal health beliefs might Seedhouse have held, given that he had had this lump for quite some time?

2. Seedhouse only brought this worry to his GP's notice when he visited to discuss other issues. Why was this? Why would he not make an appointment for that one issue?

3. The surgeon stated a 99.9% certainty for the diagnosis. What would this mean to you if you were the client?

4. Why did the appointment make Seedhouse's trepidation unavoidable?

5. Do we as health professionals, working in busy environments, take the time to realise how worried and anxious our clients might be?

6. Why would the nurse have behaved in this way?

7. Why would the surgeon behave in this way? How could this part of the consultation have been improved for the client?

8. When Seedhouse left the consultation and spoke to his wife, he was seemingly quite bewildered. How could this situation be improved for the majority of clients attending outpatient clinics?

9. What does this indicate regarding a client's health beliefs?

10. How could the anxiety caused by the bleed have been prevented?

11. Seedhouse stated: 'A doctor's moral incompetence always has a human context.' In what ways could this encounter have been managed so that it was morally competent, with as positive an outcome as possible for the client?

12. Why did Seedhouse continue on his journey towards the hospital? Did he, in actual fact, have trust in the care he was about to receive?

13. Seedhouse finally acknowledged that he was a client. Why did it take so long for him to formally acknowledge this? And why at that point?

14. How did Charleen's manner and attitude impact on Seedhouse?

15. How did the surgeon's manner and attitude impact on Seedhouse?

I want to make it clear that the statements that follow are based on my thoughts entirely. They bear no relation to actual beliefs, understandings or principles of any of the people in Seedhouse's case study. I am merely trying to prompt you to consider matters fully, looking beyond your own beliefs to gain an acceptance of the total individuality of the people we care for and those we work with.

1. What personal health beliefs might Seedhouse have held, given that he had had this lump for quite some time?

Each and every one of us holds our own very deeply felt values and beliefs, which sometimes may appear to be in contrast to those values and beliefs that we ought to uphold. As a healthcare professional, whose behaviour and choices ought to be a role model for others, I personally should make healthy choices and observe the proven recommendations for healthy eating and living. However, although I would always be an advocate of healthy choices in my professional life, in reality, in private, I do not always make those healthy choices. Despite having had a reasonably good education, an employment background in healthcare, a family history of poor health, and having experienced the deaths of many of my nearest and dearest, I still persist in making decidedly unhealthy choices in my own life. Some people follow all the health-promoting advice stoically. Others may take a more fatalistic approach, saying that they will deal with the consequences of their actions in due course. Others still may genuinely believe that it will happen to someone else, that these things (ill health) always happen to other people. It may be due to ignorance, poor education, personal experience or a multitude of other reasons, but this is a strong belief that some people hold, which prevents them from making healthy choices. As healthcare workers, we cannot blame people for the choices they make, but we need to accept that they *do* make them, and keep striving to promote the healthy choices at all times.

2. Seedhouse only brought this worry to his GP's notice when he visited to discuss other issues. Why would this have been? Why would he not make an appointment for that one issue?

There can be many unhealthy relationships in healthcare that are deep rooted, dating back to the old-fashioned approach of the days of the Biomedical Model of Health. Lay people may see the GP as a very busy person, not at all interested in their little aches and pains, and believe that the GP always has something more important to do. As lay people, my parents would only visit the GP when it was really urgent, because they did not want to bother him. The habit of not visiting the GP for each and every 'little' problem is still apparent; my own surgery has a notice in the waiting room asking clients to visit with just one issue at a time. Many people save up their 'little' issues and make one visit with them all, and often the problem that has been causing them the most concern will be raised just before the end of the consultation. This is known in the counselling profession as a 'door-knob comment'.

It is our home-grown beliefs and values that impact on our choice here. The way we have been brought up, our home-life and experiences and the impact of our education all play a part in these decision-making processes. Personally, I rarely visit my GP, and when I do I have usually already decided on the result of the consultation. It may be that I require a sick note, some antibiotics or a change of medication. Consider why this would be so. For me, this is obviously the impact of my education and training, but it is also a throwback to my childhood when my mother acted in the same way and so is part of my own specific value and belief system.

3. The surgeon stated a 99.9% certainty for the diagnosis. What would this mean to you if you were the client?

Consider the assurance the surgeon offered in which he stated the outcome with 99.9% certainty. Can we ever, in healthcare, be that certain? Is it truly ethical to offer those statistics? Having been given those figures when my first husband was diagnosed with cancer, I have first-hand experience of a similar situation. Even with my professional training, when we were told a cure was 99.9% certain, we believed it totally. We enjoyed those statistics and continued with our normal life. Three months later, a second episode gave the odds as 95% certainty, so again we believed it and trusted those words. Four months after that we were given a terminal diagnosis, being told he had months to live, as opposed to years. Still we blithely went along, allowing a timeframe in our minds of ten to eleven more months to re-organise our lives. In reality we had only six weeks. Unfortunately this has had a devastating impact on my faith in the medical profession. I believed them, and they did not give me the truth. I have reflected on this many times and now believe that false hope is the most damaging thing of all. Of course, this is very personal to me; it is affected by my own inner values and the way I was brought up with absolute faith in the medical profession, as well as my education and professional training since then.

As a healthcare professional, I am now very aware of the impact words can have on a client. They believe our words implicitly and so they need absolute truth. We should not give false hope, but neither should we terrify them with doom and gloom. The balance is very difficult to achieve, to be as honest as possible without causing unnecessary distress.

It appears to me that the ENT surgeon based his verdict on his experience with people with parotid tumours. I wonder if, when he gave those statistics, he actually considered the 0.1% that may and obviously do occur. As healthcare professionals, we give such statistics to reassure; yet by giving them we are also offering the worst possible news.

Lack of objectivity and impartiality also have to be acknowledged in my own personal experience. As the clients, we heard and took away with us the information we wanted to hear. As those with needs, we perceived that our needs were being met as we required them to be. It is hindsight that has impacted here and created some barriers that I now need to address.

4. Why did the appointment make Seedhouse's trepidation unavoidable?

I would suggest that having aired the issue with the GP, Seedhouse was again able to relegate his concern to the back of his mind. He had handed the issue over to someone more ably qualified and the longer he waited, the less he felt it to be a pressing problem. It is a kind of head-in-the-sand attitude that places the responsibility with someone else for the time being. Receiving the actual appointment brought Seedhouse back into the equation as the main character in the experience, re-awakening his anxiety because it was actually his issue, so he took the stress back on himself again. It is a natural human tendency to follow this pattern, which is almost a self-preservation strategy.

5. Do we, as health professionals, working in busy environments, take the time to realise how worried and anxious our clients might be?

How often through the course of your working day do you take the time to consider how a client may really be feeling? All healthcare areas seem to be pushed to the absolute limit in order for daily tasks to be completed. Staff numbers are at a minimum, clients always need care, and demands are made on time, resources and energy levels all the time. It is very easy to go about our business, working away, without taking the time to consider fully the thoughts and feelings of those we care for. The workplace is the usual 'habitat' for health professionals – we are there more often than we are at home, we know what to expect and how to manage ourselves, and we often forget that this can be an overwhelmingly worrying time for our clients, who are unused to the language being spoken around them (Chapter 6) and unused to the routines, furnishings and practices. We experience these things every day, and are familiar with the equipment and processes that make up the care needed. Therefore, we need to fully accept and constantly remind ourselves how strange and alarming it can be for the lay person to experience. They not only have this whole new world to contend with, but may also be very worried and frightened about the outcome of their visit.

While Seedhouse felt it was obvious that healthcare workers would consider how each and every client was feeling, do we in reality take the time to appreciate this on a daily basis?

I would suggest from a recent experience of my own that we do not continuously consider how a client in a waiting room may actually be feeling. My second husband attended a dermatology outpatient clinic after noticing a mole growing under his eyelid. Naturally, we hit the panic button because my first husband died of a malignant melanoma 10 years before that (diagnosed from a mole that appeared on his neck). Sitting in the waiting room, which was in reality a busy corridor, just two weeks before Christmas and still in the process of writing this book, I was very aware of how the staff appeared to the clients. We were naturally very apprehensive, with thoughts of cancer, radiotherapy and chemotherapy rushing through our minds, as well as how we would tell people, or manage the outcome. This all made for an uncomfortable time, waiting to be seen by the consultant. You can imagine how horrified I was by the attitude of the care staff. They did not seem to appreciate what was happening to us, their clients. Some of the nurses were discussing making bobble scarves as gifts, explaining how long they took to make and how much they cost – this did not inspire me with any confidence whatsoever. One of them, in a scruffy-looking uniform, laughingly stated that she still had to put her hair up before working. Overall, these nurses appeared careless and thoughtless with respect to the many clients in the corridor.

I acknowledge that I was fully aware of the qualifications of these nurses. During the consultation we were treated with respect and dignity and we experienced a very prompt service throughout our ordeal. However, as a retired nurse and midwife, I am appalled at how unprofessional we can appear in the workplace and wonder how we can address this to promote the caring environment we assume we automatically give.

6. Why would the nurse have behaved in this way?

It is possible that the nurse was intimidated by Seedhouse's employment status. It is equally possible that her behaviour (nervous and scurrying about) arose because of the pressures of her work. Whatever the reasons, as professional healthcare workers we need to provide an equitable service. Every client should receive the same degree of consideration and the same delivery of care from each and every health professional. We also need to be aware that clients in these kinds of situation are aware of our every move, sentence and action. This means that a five-minute consultation during our very busy working day is just that – another five-minute consultation that we manage on a daily basis. However, to the client, that five minutes can have far-reaching consequences, or even be a life-changing event. As professionals, we should be aware of their perception of us, and of how we respond to them, in order to offer the most favourable experience for the client.

7. Why would the surgeon behave in this way? How could this part of the consultation have been improved for the client?

It is possible that the ENT surgeon made a number of assumptions regarding the level of his client's knowledge and understanding. In my opinion the surgeon gained implied consent for the biopsy when Seedhouse moved to the examining table. He did not give verbal consent. Of course this is not an appropriate method of gaining consent, and it assumes too much information and knowledge from both parties involved. Think back to similar situations that you may have experienced. How often, as a healthcare worker, have you gained consent without the client verbalising it?

Consider how this part of the consultation could have been conducted in a more appropriate manner. For example, introductions are a valuable way of setting the scene and instilling confidence in clients. Using names makes them feel valued and respected, as does allowing the time and opportunity for questions. Giving information regarding procedures is necessary to ensure the client has a full understanding, and fully informed consent is a necessary part of our practice. Reflect now on the role of the nurse through this part of the process.

8. When Seedhouse left the consultation and spoke to his wife, he was seemingly quite bewildered. Thinking of other clients you meet, how could this situation be improved for the majority of clients attending outpatient clinics?

When clients are anxious and bewildered by the consultation process, the nurse present during the consultation could act as an advocate for the client. For example, the client may appreciate the presence of a family member or close friend who may be supportive and more likely to ask questions (and recall vital information later). However, this obviously needs to be balanced against the anxiety that may be caused if the nurse makes this suggestion. Reading around the subject of ethics may help your understanding here, as would discussing the issues with your work colleagues.

9. What does this indicate regarding a client's health beliefs?

Could this be part of the fatalistic health belief? That is, if it is going to happen – it will. Is this health belief common among lay people? How many of the people whose case studies you explored in Chapters 5 and 6 held this attitude towards their health? What can health professionals do, in our health promotion work, to allay this? Perhaps if the surgeon had given more information throughout this case, the underlying fear that Seedhouse held would have been greatly reduced. It is interesting, though, that even with this fear of dying, Seedhouse chose a diet drink – a healthy option.

10. How could the anxiety caused by the bleed have been prevented?

By giving all the information needed at the consultation, in verbal and written forms, the stress and worry experienced by the client could have been reduced. The problem here is how much information is right in order to reduce rather than increase anxiety. Every client we meet has different needs regarding these issues; therefore it is not a cure-all remedy we are seeking but a way of ensuring that all clients are treated in the most appropriate way for their own situation. Some clients need to know and can safely assimilate the information. For others, the less they know, the better they manage the experience. This is a fine balance and there is no easy solution. Building a strong relationship with a client will ease this process, but the high turnover of clients in outpatient clinics makes it difficult to build such relationships.

11. Seedhouse stated: 'A doctor's moral incompetence always has a human context.' In what ways could this encounter have been managed so that it was morally competent, with as positive an outcome as possible for the client?

Mutual respect between the professional and the client would have promoted the development of trust and sharing of appropriate information. The employment of good, empathic communication skills might have resulted in full understanding of the situation. Improved time management could have enabled this to happen.

12. Why did Seedhouse continue on his journey towards the hospital? Did he, in actual fact, have trust in the care he was about to receive?

This is reminiscent of a time long ago when the doctor was seen as the 'all-knowing' oracle who had to be obeyed. Fortunately, today the relationships among the members of the multidisciplinary team involve far more mutual respect and this needs to cascade to encompass all our clients too.

13. Seedhouse finally acknowledged that he was a client – why did it take so long for him to formally acknowledge this? And why at this point?

Denial is a very strong emotion when we are faced with difficult situations, particularly a health issue like this. Seedhouse presumably felt well in himself, and was able to function normally at work, attending sports events and so on. It was only when faced with the reality of the procedure that he finally acknowledged it was actually happening to him. As healthcare professionals, we need to understand these emotions and be aware of the often delayed impact on our clients.

14. How did Charleen's manner and attitude impact on Seedhouse?

It is my impression here that Charleen kept herself very separate from the lived experience of the client, although it is not easy to understand why that would be so. She performed her duties almost by rote, barely engaging with Seedhouse. A client in this position needs information and to be continually reassured, so a narrative by Charleen of what she was doing would have supported the client throughout. It would have led to an opportunity for the client to ask questions and for Charleen to reinforce health-promoting activities.

15. How did the surgeon's manner and attitude impact on Seedhouse?

I cannot imagine any healthcare worker not offering reassurance when a client is being admitted for a procedure. Whatever the procedure, we are all well aware that the impact on the client is far greater than the impact on ourselves. Unless we are totally unfeeling, we automatically offer reassurance and explain our own actions and the actions of others throughout the interaction. As nurses or healthcare workers, we automatically become an advocate for each and every client we meet. This means we need to be tuned in to that client's needs and ensure they are met appropriately. If someone is being negligent and not making sure that those needs are met, then we need to encourage the appropriate care in a suitable manner. As healthcare workers, we should consider our position carefully, employ a professional attitude and respect the individuality of all those we meet during our working day. I can only imagine that, in Seedhouse's case, Charleen (maybe the doctor too) was having a bad day, although this does not excuse the poor practice.

Here are some other points you may wish to reflect on regarding Seedhouse's experience with the ENT surgeon.

Seedhouse felt he would be 'making a fuss' if he asked questions, but are clients 'making a fuss' if they question our actions? How can we ensure that they do not feel this way? Seedhouse was obviously in shock following the biopsy, but how often do we consider the impact of an invasive procedure? How can situations like this be improved? The ENT surgeon in this scenario also commented on the state of the public system. Do you feel this could have been perceived as blaming the client for not having the appropriate insurance? When the surgeon suggested that Seedhouse could seek private care for the procedure, did he make an assumption regarding the client's financial position?

Seedhouse said that he 'reeled out of the ward unable to think straight'. How would you feel if one of your clients left your work area in this state? Consider, too, the impact of entering a room full of medical equipment, suspecting (but not knowing) that something is going to be 'done' to you, without any of it being explained. Just how often do we take the time to explain equipment that is familiar to us but which can be daunting to an anxious client?

I am fortunate in that I have engaged in correspondence with David Seedhouse while compiling this chapter. Once I had written the first draft, I sent it to him for his comments and he replied with some very useful feedback. He suggested that, even if we really try to see a situation from the perspective of others (that is, our clients), we still cannot truly see things from their actual perspective. Seedhouse went on to say:

> 'Clearly we should be respectful and offer explanations (we can do this), clearly we should try to be sensitive to the feelings of worried patients (good health workers can do this) and ideally we should try to understand the depth of patient's concerns (but we cannot always achieve this, however much we try, because so much of other's lives are hidden from all of us), and, because we cannot know the depth of other people's lives, we should tentatively, in an exploratory way, try to find out where hurts and where support would be best, rather in the way you do when you are becoming friends with a person and do not want to risk the new friendship.'

Seedhouse, 2011

We need to acknowledge and accept that, although we wish to give the best and most appropriate care or service to each and every one of the clients we meet, we cannot ever know everything there is to know about them. Each person is, as we are, totally individual, with individual values and beliefs, and individual factors that impact on those values and beliefs. We all share a certain amount of personal information and we all withhold information (for a variety of reasons) and naturally these opposite ends of the spectrum affect the way we behave in any given situation. In relation to our clients, we need to accept the complexity of the relationship and should be open to the fact that we can never know all there is to know about them. Yet we should offer understanding and empathy towards them at all times.

This chapter has provided a huge amount of food for thought, and I hope that students will work through it carefully, exploring the values, beliefs and relationships that we can all improve, all the time. Material such as this is not static; it cannot be learnt by reading it, then putting it away. It needs constant thought and revisiting to ensure that the lessons learnt keep being added to. Eventually I hope that students will be able to bring out more issues from the case study, or substitute material of their own for consideration.

Values and beliefs are an intrinsic part of each and every one of us, and they grow and change as we move through life. As healthcare workers, we need to constantly consider how these affect ourselves and our colleagues but mainly our clients.

Chapter eight
Graduation Day and Beyond

The successful completion of the foundation degree programme culminates in a ceremony conducted by the university. For students at Lincoln University, the ceremony takes place at Lincoln Cathedral, a grand building full of history and charm. Adorned in caps and gowns, the students parade before the Dean of the university to receive the award of a Foundation Degree in Health and Social Care Practice. Then they celebrate together, taking refreshments with family, friends and teaching staff. It is a very special day, a chance to show off and revel in achievements that can be shared with the family and friends who have given their support and encouragement over two years.

By this stage, you will be well on the way to becoming a lifelong learner. Your learning is not complete because in reality we never stop learning. Getting this award marks the beginning of practice as a professional healthcare worker, and you will start to consolidate that learning with practice. There needs to be a disclaimer here though: study at this level can create a thirst for more, so this might be the ideal opportunity to enquire about taking your award to the next level, to a full degree. The number of my students who say on the final day of the programme 'No more study for me' greatly exceeds the number who decide to continue studying – but on graduation day the numbers are reversed, with more students choosing to complete the full BSc or BA in various disciplines, or courses within the workplace, or to carry out action research to improve practice in their workplace.

For all the students I have worked with to date, the programme and the award itself is life-changing. They have all made a difficult but rewarding journey, and emerged as strong practitioners who are a credit to themselves, to those they work with, and to their families and friends. I wish them all every success in the future.

References

Buzan, T. and Buzan, B. (2003). *The Mind Map Book*. London, BBC Worldwide.

Hendrick, J. (2004). *Law and Ethics. Foundations in Nursing and Health Care.* Cheltenham, Nelson Thornes.

Jeffers, S. (1987). *Feel the Fear and Do It Anyway.* London, Vermilion.

Moonie, N., Nolan, Y. and Lavers, S. (2003). *BTEC First Caring,* 2nd edn. Oxford, Heinemann.

Northedge, A. (1990). *The Good Study Guide*. The Open University. Devon, Polestar Wheatons.

Rogers, W.A. (1992). *Managing Teacher Stress*. Essex, Pearson Education.

Seedhouse, D. (2009). *Ethics: The Heart of Health Care*, 3rd edn. West Sussex, Wiley-Blackwell.

Seedhouse, D. (2011). Personal email to Margaret Bannister.

Sussex, F., Herne, D. and Scourfield, P. (2008). *Advanced Health and Social Care for NVQ/SVQ Foundation Degrees*. Essex, Heinemann.

Sussex, F., Herne, D. and Scourfield, P. (2008). *Advanced Health and Social Care for NVQ/SVQ and Foundation Degrees*. Essex, Heinemann.

Further reading

Buzan, T. and Buzan, B. (2003). *The Mind Map Book*. London, BBC Worldwide.

Frankland, A. and Sanders, P. (1995). *Next Steps in Counselling*. Herefordshire, PCCS Books.

Freshwater, D. (2003). *Counselling Skills for Nurses, Midwives and Health Visitors.* Berkshire, Open University Press.

Godfrey, J. (2009). *Palgrave Study Skills. How to Use Your Reading in Your Essays.* Hampshire, Palgrave Macmillan.

Hendrick, J. (2004). *Law and Ethics. Foundations in Nursing and Health Care.* Cheltenham, Nelson Thornes.

Jasper, M. (2000). *Beginning Reflective Practice. Foundations in Nursing and Health Care*. Cheltenham, Nelson Thornes.

Jeffers, S. (1987). *Feel the Fear and Do It Anyway*. London, Vermilion.

Koch, T. and Kralik, D. (2006). *Participatory Action Research in Health Care*. Oxford, Blackwell Publishing.

Levin, P. (2004). *Student-Friendly Guides. Write Great Essays! Reading and Essay Writing for Undergraduates and Taught Postgraduates*. Berkshire, Open University Press.

McMillan, K. and Weyers, J. (2007). *How to Write Essays and Assignments*. Essex, Pearson Education.

Moonie, N., Nolan,Y. and Lavers, S. (2003). *BTEC First in Caring,* 2nd edn. Oxford, Heinemann.

Myers. B, and Shaw, L. (2004). *Access to HE: The Social Sciences.* Cheltenham, Nelson Thornes.

Northedge, A. (1990). *The Good Study Guide.* The Open University. Devon, Polestar Wheatons.

Page, M. and Winstanley, C. (2009). *Writing Essays for Dummies*. West Sussex, John Wiley and Sons.

Race, P. (2005). *Making Learning Happen. A Guide for Post-Compulsory Education.* London, Sage Publications.

Seedhouse, D. (2009). *Ethics: The Heart of Health Care*, 3rd edn. West Sussex, Wiley-Blackwell.

Soles, D. (2005). *The Academic Essay. How to Plan, Draft, Write and Revise.* A Studymates Series. Somerset, Studymates.

Sussex, F., Herne, D. and Scourfield, P. (2008). *Advanced Health and Social Care for NVQ/SVQ and Foundation Degrees. Essex, Heinemann.*

Woods, B. (2000). *Basics of Psychology*, 2nd edn. Oxford, Hodder Education.

Index